# AFTER NORA

## Penelope Curtis

This first English-language edition published by Les Fugitives editions in the United Kingdom in April 2024 • Les Fugitives Ltd, 91 Cholmley Gardens, Fortune Green Road, London NW6 1UN • www.lesfugitives.com • Cover design by Sarah Schulte & Dominic Lee • Text design by MacGuru Ltd • All rights reserved • No part of this publication may be reproduced, stored in a retrieval system or transmitted in any form or by any means, electronic, mechanical, photocopying, recording or otherwise, without prior permission in writing from Les Fugitives editions • A CIP catalogue record for this book is available from the British Library • The rights of Penelope Curtis to be identified as author of this work have been identified in accordance with Section 77 of the Copyright, Designs and Patents Act 1988 • Printed in England by CMP, Poole, Dorset • ISBN: 978-1-7397783-4-7 • The divorce notice on p.34 is from the Uxbridge and West Drayton Gazette, Friday 12 November 1926, p.20, © 2023 Newspapers.com • The 1923 Map on p.22 © Jordans Village Limited archives • Photographs by Dominic Lee.

Les Fugitives

London

*In memory of two women who died too soon,*
*Nora Curtis and Maria de Sousa.*

*This book tells two separate but related stories. Part 2 recreates the story of Adam Curtis, my father, and his relationship with Maria de Sousa, whom he met when I was a child. Part 1 concerns his mother Nora, whom I never knew but whose paintings I grew up with. I imagine her as a woman who was serious about trying to find a place for painting in her life.*

# Part I

## CHAPTER ONE

*Two Herberts*

At the close of the year 1925 Nora Cundall and her husband made their way to the Chelsea Arts Club Ball. For weeks Nora had encouraged her husband to accept the tickets his brother Charles had offered, and although he worried the place might be too noisy, and that it might be difficult to get home, in the end he gave in. Nora and Herbert had met at the very same Ball in 1919. The theme then was 'Dazzle', which, picking up on the camouflage painted by artists for the armed forces during the Great War, was perfectly pitched to celebrate the end of hostilities, if not the return to normality. Charles Cundall had had a spare ticket and a brother; Nora Stevens needed a partner. What began as a convenient arrangement between two fellow artists took on a more permanent status when, not long after, Herbert Cundall proposed to Nora. Somewhat taken aback, not least because she had blamed herself for not thinking of how ill-suited the evening's entertainment would be to a conscientious objector, she nonetheless heard herself saying yes to his second proposal.

Herbert Cundall was very different from his brother, but one could still see that they came from the same family. Not so much in the way they looked, but rather because they shared a particular upbringing: Northern English, with a touch of foreign glamour (their father had been a Manila merchant). If Charles had continued to travel, Herbert had instead been more serious-minded, and his wish to marry was surely part of this. Nora felt as if she had been part of a scheme – if only vaguely sketched out in dullish tones – to reclaim a place in England. She also knew, or was obliged to admit, that she too had wanted a place. She had been waiting long enough for the war to end; at the age of 29 she felt she had to take her chance.

This year the theme was elaborately medieval, with plenty of opportunity for cross-dressing. Nora, a robust woman with dark hair, strong colouring and what were often described as 'apple cheeks', dressed up in Arthurian guise, wearing a hand-painted "Guinevere" dress with blue and red ribbons in her chignons. Her husband declined to dress up fully, leaving that to the artists. He deigned instead to wear a kimono in place of his dinner jacket. It may be that this outfit attracted more notice than he would have wanted, as a number of young men, in masks, seemed to head over to him remarkably quickly. Perhaps it was the combination of conventional evening dress with something quite unconventional, and worn with an air of diffident anxiety, which proved so appealing.

Before long, amid the multiple coulisses of the Royal Albert Hall, Nora found herself detached from her husband, talking to an architect who was also called Herbert. She vaguely remembered that her family had sent him some parcels (a cake; some

books?) when he was on the French front. There was
a Masonic link, if she had it right, between her father
and his. Thin, even emaciated, his sapphire-coloured
eyes pressed into her and she was immediately attracted. While her husband was otherwise detained,
they exchanged some crucial information, and within
a short time they had made a date to meet for tea the
following week.

*

They met in the Lyons Corner House café near Piccadilly Circus. He asked her what she was addicted
to, and she knew more or less at once that he found
her attractive too. She could not think how best to
answer, or how honest to be. What did he want to
hear? Why was he asking such a forward question?
She looked for a way to be honest and proper, and
said, baths. She did not ask him the same question
back, fearing it might lead to immediate complica-
tions. Instead they talked about ordinary things, but
with a sense of rising anticipation.

She wrote to him at his office, saying she would like
to meet again. They went for a walk in Green Park,
and sat on a bench near the lake. He was unsettled
and even gloomy. She was reassuring, although she
knew no more than he how this could be resolved.
She patted him on the back, almost maternally, as
if the problem was his, not hers. They looked dully
at the waterfowl and the rain began to fall, gently.
Neither had an umbrella and she allowed him to take

her arm and escort her to shelter. They stood under a tree and he lit a cigarette for her from his own. They smoked in silence. He went on holding her by the elbow. She said she must go, and he took her to the Underground station. He stood on the platform, took off his hat, and put it back on as her train departed.

A week later they had lunch together. She knew already that she enjoyed his company. She found herself telling him things she had rarely, if ever, told anyone. She also wanted to be amusing, to amuse him. He seemed to enjoy her stories. She told him little about her life at home, and spoke mainly about her childhood in Dublin, about her parents, about learning to draw, and paint. But he pressed her on occasion, and before so very long they were talking about more serious matters. Why did she not tell her husband what she had told him?

They went to sit in the park, and because the weather was clement, and because they did not know what to do, or what to say, or how long for, he hired two deckchairs. She had never before sat on a hired deckchair in a park, and did not know whether it mattered. He reached out and held her hand. They sat side by side and looked at the other people as if they could never be like them. When she got up, he gave her the deck chair receipts. She assumed they were a kind of souvenir.

The next day she had word from him:

'Don't miss me please it was nice today and we laughed about our strange predicament. It can't be improved so we have to enjoy what we have which is rather a lot. I will think of you regularly and so you have no need to miss me I'm going nowhere.'

She put the receipts in a decorated saucer on her dressing table. When her husband queried them she was unable to satisfactorily explain their presence. He told her he wondered what she was up to and she told him she agreed. Now things became both clearer and more complicated. As Nora wondered about her motivations, she wondered also about what she was ready to give up.

*London Town*

They met on occasion, and if the weather was nice, walked in the parks, sitting, very often, on the very same benches. They began to find stories which reminded them of their own. She was offered tickets to see *La Traviata* and urged him to come with her. She wanted him to be beside her, in public, but indoors, cossetted in velvet seats, close, warm, sensual, all in a way that was permissible. She was growing tired of benches. They made her feel somehow alien, in a way that she would never have foreseen. They used to seem so friendly, but now benches only echoed her own predicament, being on the wrong side of life.

Even before they went inside the Opera House she knew she was excited. She saw him leaning against a pillar on the piazza, and walked slowly forward. He kissed her hand, and her fingers, drawing them to his lips. Already at the interval their eyes were moist, and this was unusually acceptable. At the end, as tears rolled down their faces, they revelled in the licence. He took her by Underground to the station. They cried there too, safe in the knowledge that they were crying for the same reasons and with the same intensity, about themselves, and no longer about Rodolfo and Violetta. He took her onto the platform, opened the door of the train, looked as if he might walk off, and suddenly kissed her. He kissed her as if he were jumping on board.

He wrote her a note: 'But in case you can't imagine it, I think of you a lot. You are extraordinary. The kisses were very special, sunshine through clouds a moment in life's wonder. I can never give you the companionship you should have but being a close friend is something. I looked at Violetta's story having previously paid no attention to opera plots and as you observed once again the men are unreliable.' He wrote her another, 'An aria from the Mikado at breakfast. A letter from you makes me think of moths and candles'.

*

Every few days she received a card, a short note, hastily written, from somewhere on his way to work. Usually she opened the envelope on the doorstep, standing on the doormat, with the tendrils of the wisteria and the old beech leaves blowing in. With his words she criss-crossed London, feeling its weather.

'Sitting by the canal. It's a bit chilly. Work,

commitments, obligations, crowd in. But in the little space between you're there – coals to Newcastle for me but the lady insists. I'll be asking her for a guided tour of the galleries next.'

'Message from London Fields low sun crows cawing. Thanks for my xxxs they're always too quick.'

'Glad to hear I can transport you. I go to these quiet places to spend time talking to you. It's as good as it's going to get.'

'Tender message from the New River under a walnut tree. Ophelia. Have seen you in spirit. I like sleeping in trains. You bring out an unusually romantic strain in me but when it eventually bores you, you must say I can dig something else up.'

'I miss you and feel sad that I have created a situation I can't control or improve. I would like it if you would tell me how you are.'

'On top of Parliament Hill talking about Constable and the English landscape garden. No I didn't get a postcard. Can't think where you sent it.'

'Thought I'd try streets instead, a kerb for a bench. Chose Aran Walk for the Irish connection. Cold here time for a scarf. Belle Iseult though she's taller than you.'

'Swept up by the crowd it's not the same speaking to you from pedestrian places.'

'*C'est moi l'homme qui t'aime. Quatre jours sans toi est difficile. J'aimerais te voir ce soir sitôt que possible.*'

He met her at Marylebone station. On her journey she tried not to think about meeting him but could not help but imagine him at the barrier, ready to embrace her. When she arrived she could not even see him, and then realised he was there, his back against the wall, looking at the roof. He told her how much he loved station architecture. She did not make the obvious retort, but stood back, holding her bag in front of her, and asked him to explain just what it was he liked so much. Together they looked at the ironwork and the spans, the tracery across the space. She realised she had been caught out, never having looked much at the roof, and having expected instead that he would be looking at her.

They walked down to Bruton Place because Nora wanted to see the new exhibition at the Beaux Arts

Gallery. Quite a number of women artists were there, sculptors as well as painters. Nora wondered about this, and about herself. Although the landscapes by the male painters were closer to what she was doing, she found herself drawn to the works by women, different as they were. Some extremely so. She wondered if she too could get to that point, and by what route. It made her feel optimistic, and despairing.

They went back to Marylebone by way of the Wallace Collection. Herbert wanted to look at the clocks. Nora found a few pictures which spoke to her on that damp grey day, but felt a little oppressed. She seemed to be surrounded by images of mistresses and objects created for mistresses. She wondered whether or not she would become a mistress. Would she be a mistress if her lover was not married? And she was? In any case she wondered if and how it might happen. As they went out into the darkening square and the drizzle, she held his arm more tightly, but also felt more distant. He was walking in a matter-of-fact way, briskly. He did not look at her; did not respond to her pressure.

*

Some weeks later they went to the cinema to see *Chartres*, a film which Herbert had read a little about and had just been made by a young French film director. It was very short. They both enjoyed it for different reasons; Herbert for the many different views of architectural details which even he, with his sharp eyes, had never been able to see, and Nora because of the leaves in the birch trees suddenly trembling, breaking the stillness of the stones. She thought it was odd to make a moving film about a building that never moved. It ended, however, with views of the war memorials on the city ramparts, and Nora worried about that. About its effect on the man beside her.

*Chartres* was followed by a much longer film called *Maldone*, named after a man obsessed by Zita the gypsy, even after his marriage to Flora. The scenes of dancing, whirling around seen from above, made Nora feel dizzy, their hypnotic quality exacerbated by Herbert's almost incessant stroking of her forearm. He became as restless as the protagonist, crossing and re-crossing his long thin legs, shifting around in his seat, as if he were being bitten. Nora looked at him and wondered what was happening: a return to the war, an account of a conventional marriage, an alternative view of passion, an abrupt reckoning with its impossibility? What was making the man beside her so agitated? He would not say, and she would not ask, but it seemed as if he was working himself up.

*

At home Nora started to amass the notes which were delivered after her husband had gone to work. Normally she found them on the doormat; occasionally the postman caught her in the doorway and handed them to her directly. She would hold his eye, just briefly, weighing up his assessment of their frequency. She kept them in her handkerchief holder, sometimes going upstairs after lunch to marvel at their number and style. She knew they flattered her, but she also believed them, and revelled in their unambiguous desire to please.

'It's the man who loves you in English here. Thank you for giving your evening to me.'

'Out of the window is the spire of Antwerp cathedral. It is very delicate.'

'In the Fields there are church bells. Now it's crows. A moment of peace thinking of your voice.'

'In the Fields in the shadow of an old plane beautiful light. It would be nice to disturb you.'

'Glad to hear you're meeting more architects. I know you have a soft spot for them. But I wonder why we are communicating like this. For me a limit is to stay mainly on the subject of you.'

'Anticipating your reply is distracting to my real life – you will tell me I am not consistent.'

'Will see you over a white tablecloth.'

\*

They met at Piccadilly Circus and went to The York Minster. They were offered a good table and chose a worse one; they both wanted to be closer together. She wanted to feel his voice in her ear; he wanted to bathe in her luminescence. They charted and located territories on the margins of their real lives, largely finding places to settle among books and paintings. But sometimes they tired, almost simultaneously, of this effort, and came up short. Then he put his hand on her hand, admiring her lustrous brown skin, contrasting his bony fingers with hers. Whatever she chose to eat, he chose too. They were not a young couple, but felt as if the waiters wanted to indulge them as if they were, allowing them extra time and extra space. It was as if everyone and everything was complicit, and she liked it just so.

\*

'Thank you for your company. It's so strange and wonderful to kiss you I hardly know how to. It's so different but it felt like a French evening. Sun's out I had better get moving.'

'Morning sun in the busy park. Capability Brown had the advantage of a lot of men. Thinking about you as usual.'

'I hope you are at the Opera with someone you like and that you have some good adventures. Au revoir amour.'

'Sliding through the grey clean city thinking of you almost forgot where I was.'

'Grey light feeling a bit numb on the park bench.'

'The same bench these days a quiet spot in the middle of the fields, a few dogs.'

'Same spot same things waiting for Spring'.

\*

Nora went to the zoo to draw. It was one of her favourite activities. She liked to draw the big lazy animals who never moved, as well as the tree-loving lemurs who curled their tails around the branches. It was a place where she found she could forget the problems associated with being a woman, and an artist, and a wife. In a way too she also identified with the animals, feeling her power, and her inertia, her inability to act. Herbert came to find her there one morning in the spring. She was sitting on a small folding stool. He came upon her from behind and whispered in her ear: 'You are beautiful. And I love you'. He upset her watercolour palette as she reacted in shock, and before she was able to save it, he was kissing her neck. As she gathered up the pieces, and the little tablets of paint, he put his arms around her and pulled her up. 'I need you to stay with me', he said, 'I cannot bear it to be otherwise.'

*Baldock*

She told her husband about the letters, and about the meetings. He sent her home to stay with her mother and reflect on her behaviour, as if she were a child. This did not help Nora's mood. Her mother lived in Baldock, an hour north of London, and so she spent three weeks there 'considering her situation'. She was 36 years old. Her parents did not know what to say, and she did not want them to say anything, so she painted them. She painted her mother during the day and her father in the evening. She had brought her paints with her. She had no canvas to hand, but she found pieces of hardboard in the garden shed. She asked her mother to sit comfortably, beside the window, and made some sketches first. Her mother was wearing her apron over her everyday clothes. Her father was still wearing the clothes in which he came home from work, so his appearance was formal. They did not look as if they belonged together. Apart from that, Nora gardened, trying not so much to consider her situation, as to let her situation speak to her. She dug over the garden behind the house and weeded it thoroughly. She found a general retailer where she bought bone meal, and a seed merchant, where she bought half ounces of bean, spinach, beetroot and turnip seeds. She sprinkled the meal on the earth and dug it over again. Then she dug small trenches where she laid the seed, three or four inches apart and at a depth of 2 inches. She covered the trenches over and watered them. She found little canes which she put at either end of each trench with the name of the vegetable. She hoped that she would be in London by the time the seeds germinated.

Nora reflected. On her early years in Dublin, her schooling in London, Charles, the artist she had met, first, and his brother, the man she had married. Herbert Cundall was a little older than Nora, and a little older than his artistic brother. Their youngest brother Walter died at Gallipoli. Charles himself was shot in the arm. He had to relearn how to paint. Though they were all brought up as Quakers, only

Herbert had not enlisted. She had admired that then. Herbert and Nora had moved to Buckinghamshire as soon as they married, right after the war, in order to be among the founder members of a new Quaker village, Jordans, designed by Frederick Rowntree. It had been an adventure at that time, which, for them, at least, hadn't lasted very long. When she looked at the map in Jordans, and saw their plot, marked out in ink, with their name, she could only just remember the thrill of the early days. A completely new village, each member creating a part of a whole, a shared plan. Herbert's Quaker schooling played into his picture of their future. But Nora had soon begun to see that Herbert hadn't thought very much about living together when he proposed to her. She also knew that she had been guilty of wanting something in her life to happen, after waiting so long, and that Jordans gave them both a kind of answer.

She was not so very young but she had allowed herself to be led into an improbable future. Herbert had set up a little studio for his wife at the back of the house, on Puers Lane, but she never felt at home there. It was a nice studio, but somehow in the wrong place. It made her feel that her work was no more than a pastime. It seemed to confirm that her husband did not understand. Quite often she used to go with him in his car to the station and take the fast train up to town to get away from Jordans. When she returned he collected her at the station. When she forgot to phone him at the bank, and he had to come out from home, he was irritable, and she was not surprised. But somehow she

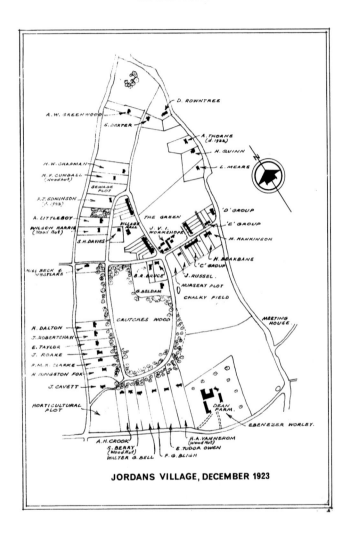

**JORDANS VILLAGE, DECEMBER 1923**

couldn't apologise, and his testy mood was only exacerbated by hers. Either she would tell him all about an
exhibition she had attended, which she knew meant
little or nothing to him, or she would simply say that
nothing much had happened, and she didn't know
why she had bothered to make the journey. She knew
that this was inadequate, and she did not know why
she could not bring herself to expand upon it.

They would drive the rest of the way home in
silence, and on arrival, she would take off her things
and go through at once to their bedroom. He would
remain next door, uncertain, and she would be set
apart, certain. She got into bed and turned out the
light. After a while he would follow suit, sometimes
manoeuvring himself in beside her, but, as often as
not, going to sleep on the settee. Before so very long
they had separate beds, and apart from moments
when they talked about Jordans or about the news,
rarely shared much at all. The simple little house
was ill-fitted to two people who were not getting on,
and their proximity was irksome. Nora liked nothing
about it now except the setting. Only the trees soothed
her; only their little greenhouse gave her relief.

Going to the ball had reminded Nora of what she
had missed. Company. Grandeur. Fun. Sympathy.
She was in a mood to leave the Quakers behind, get
away from the countryside, the little made-up village.
The village green, with its flat expanse of invented
common, felt claustrophobic. Only the old meeting
house was authentic; everything else felt like a bit of
town transported to the country. But it was not really

the place that was the problem. Perhaps it was not even her husband. It was surely that she had fallen in love with the other Herbert. His lean, distant persona fascinated her. She did not feel that she knew him, not yet, and probably never would. But she liked that. And she liked the fact that after so long being alone, he had at last found someone: her. His certainty had caused her to act. It was she who was taking the risk, but she felt that it was he who had made the decision.

There was no question in her mind about returning to her husband. She wondered about these years of marriage, provoked she supposed by the war, the loss of so many men, Herbert's connections, and his convictions too. Like the other young men she knew, Herbert had been a Conscientious Objector, and their location in Jordans shielded them from the worst of the opprobrium, but it also meant that they felt separated from other people in this, becoming the subject of disdain. A new Quaker village was something special, she knew they had both felt, especially in 1919, but perhaps their combined distance from the war wasn't helpful. And in the end the village turned out to be quite ordinary. Even the architecture, supposedly so new, seemed old fashioned to her. In any case, she had decided to focus on the fact that she liked this new Herbert a lot more than the old. He seemed to understand her, but to withhold this from her, in a way that appealed. She liked his thinness, the experience – unknowably but surely bitter – which he carried with him, and she liked his learning.

*

Nora received a letter from her husband, care of her parents. In fact the cover note was to her father. Her father gave both parts to Nora to read, and she went into the garden, sat on the bench by the door, and opened the envelope.

'Dear Mr. Stevens
I am most grateful to you for taking Nora in while she reconsiders. I very much regret what has happened, and trust that now sufficient time has elapsed she will feel ready to return to her own home. I should be grateful if you would pass the enclosed note to her.
Yours most sincerely
    Herbert Cundall'


    'Dear Nora
I have been thinking a lot about what you said, and I hope that now you can put it behind you and come back to Jordans. I understand that you may have got bored here and I shall try to find ways to make life more interesting for you. Remember all that you and I have invested in being here, and I hope you will not throw it away. The village is looking very nice at present and I am sure people will be pleased to see you back and will say nothing about your absence.
Affectionately yours
    Herbert'

Nora read the letter with a kind of disgust and put it back in the envelope. She thought it hardly worth responding to. She could just see Herbert at his desk, with his headed paper, unscrewing his fountain pen in readiness. She could see his well-pressed clothes. She even imagined him dressing for the occasion. She could see him not even thinking about her. But she knew her father would ask about the letter, as soon as he came back from work. She wondered what he himself thought, given the abrupt complacency which she could also discern in the letter addressed to him. She went indoors and got a sheet of paper and a pen from her father's desk. She took it upstairs and sat beside her bedroom window to compose a response.

'Dear Herbert
You sent me home and I have stayed here. I have not had to reconsider because I had already made up my mind. I will not come back to Jordans. I presume that now you will divorce me.
Yours
   Nora'

Another letter arrived.

'Dear Nora
I am sorry to read your reply. If you do not wish to come to Jordans, may we please meet? I have no wish to divorce you and would prefer that we put this episode behind us.
Yours truly

Herbert'

Nora sent her answer by telegram: 'Will leave for Seaford soonest'.

### *Seaford*

And so Nora and her chosen Herbert arranged to go to a hotel in Seaford, where, he had told her, he would arrange for a friend of his to make a report and to ascertain that they had been caught in flagrante. This was a strange way to consummate a nascent love affair, and it made everything feel pre-ordained. They took the train together from Victoria Station. Each had a small bag with overnight things. They smoked a lot and said little. For a short stretch he recited Macaulay's 'How Horatio held the Bridge', keeping time with the sound of the wheels on the track.

> '*Lars Porsena of Clusium,*
> By the Nine Gods he swore,
> That the great house of Tarquin
> Should suffer wrong no more.
> By the Nine Gods he swore it,
> and named a trysting-day,
> And bade his messengers ride forth,
> East, and west, and south and north,
> To summon his array.
> East and west and south and north,
> His messengers ride fast
> And town and town and cottage,
> Have heard the trumpet's blast.'

Nora was impressed by the pounding rhythm but found it tiresome. Herbert said that was what he liked; that it was irresistible. He was surprised that she didn't know it already, but they agreed it was probably a poem that was taught to boys rather than to girls. Nora could recite 'I know a bank where the wild thyme blows', unknown to him. He had never heard her evince any such knowledge of literature and she affirmed that it was learned by heart, as homework. She thought too of 'The quality of mercy' as she embarked upon a course that went against her upbringing, and her education.

At the hotel they booked into separate rooms and each went to rest. She took off her shoes, and then lay on the soft mattress thinking of what was to come. She crossed her hands on her breast and crossed her ankles. She tried to breathe deeply and evenly. She could hear the seagulls outside, and the occasional shriek of a child. The hotel was neither nice nor nasty, just a place to stay a night. She thought about her husband, and about the way in which he tended to introduce her, as if he owned her. She thought about how he made love, or didn't, and how involved he was with the Quakers. She thought about their arguments, and how they ended. She thought about how he snored.

On waking she saw that the light was fading. She got up, smoothed down her dress and pulled up her stockings, washed her face and looked in the mirror. Then she took her cardigan and her bag, closed the door and knocked on the adjacent one. Herbert answered quickly and asked her if she would like to have a drink. No? Something to eat? What might they find? They could go and take a look.

They walked along the seafront with nothing to say to each other. In the end, listlessly, they found another hotel where they could have some dinner, and something to drink. The waiter was delightful and lightened their mood. Herbert ordered a brandy and she had some too. Then he took her hand and with quick determination, pulled her along the pavement back to where they were staying.

He opened the door of his room with his key, and stood aside to let her in. It was very like her room, but the bed was untouched, and the window was open. An ashtray was already full of cigarette stubs. On top of his small suitcase was a copy of the *Times Literary Supplement*, folded, and a sketchbook with a drawing of the view. She studied it, briefly, and looked round at him. 'It's good, isn't it, this drawing?' He smiled, quite mischievously, holding her by the shoulders. She steadied, and he took off her hat. Putting it on the bed behind him, he said, 'It will all be alright, I promise'.

She took a short sharp inward breath and bent down to take off her shoes and stockings. She stood beside him in her bare feet, feeling a little stocky. He took off his shirt and she could see how thin he was. He inclined his head to reach her lips and kissed her suddenly, deeply, and for a long time. She exhaled. They each took off their own clothes and she got in under the sheets. Her dark hair was half up and half down. He pulled the sheets abruptly off her and lay close beside her. He kissed her again and again, and she almost forgot that they were here as a proof of guilt.

*

Nora returned to Baldock. For some reason – moral, superstitious, or other – Nora had not written to her new Herbert while she had been at home. Nor had she heard from him. This was quite a contrast after his steady stream of notes. Back in Baldock she felt suddenly very alone. And rather foolish too. She had not thought about this part. She knew she needed to talk to her parents about her decisions, but she also knew that they would not want to give her advice. When her father came back he suggested they take a walk to look at the dig that was going on in Walls Field. It wasn't far, and it was of great significance. Nora was quite ready to be persuaded. They put on their hats and coats and went out towards the Clothall Road.

The light was good and the weather fair. Nora discovered her father had been following the story of the dig, even though he knew little about archaeology. It was, he told her, quite a find. They smiled together. A farmer had turned up some clay vessels there when he was ploughing. Since then her father had come along a few times to see how they were getting along, and had gone to hear a lantern slide lecture given by the curator of the local museum, who thought that Baldock was a lost Roman town.

When they arrived Nora was surprised to see a small group of people with spades, women and men, digging. Her father had obviously encountered them before, because he went over at once and began talking. Then he introduced her to Mr. Westell, the curator. Mr Westell suggested that she might like to join in, if she had time on her hands. Baldock was much older than they had all thought, and much more interesting. Nora was indeed tempted, for a moment, to forget the present and turn to the past. And the quality of the finds was exceptional, Mr Westell said. He asked her if she had been to see them already in the museum at Letchworth. She said no. He could send her an off-print of his article, if she was at all interested. Nora said it was very kind of him, but it wasn't really something she could get very involved in. Her father said, 'But you could send it to me. My daughter has other things on her mind'.

Nora was thinking about love-making and divorcing. Although she and Herbert had wanted to be together, they also both did not want to, not there and then. It was a relief to feel him so close, but a disappointment to feel it had to be done, and quickly. She wanted to enjoy something she had never had before; wanting him more, finding him attractive, and loving him too. As soon as the sun had come up that morning, he had sat up abruptly and gone to look through the windows. She tried to cajole him to come back to bed, but he didn't want to. He washed quickly and got dressed. She watched him shaving as if it were a rare and unexpected custom, doting on the process of lathering, shaving, rinsing and drying. She raised her arms towards him to coax him back towards her, but he stood apart, resolute, and said he was going downstairs. How could it be that he was so abrupt; untempted either by her body, or by her pleading? She saw that she too must get up and leave the scene of their 'crime'. Without sentimentality.

She told her father that her trip to Seaford had decided the future. Her father asked her if that meant she had made a decision. Nora said she had, but didn't know what it meant in the short term. That is why she had to go down again to talk it through. Her father asked if she minded telling him what decision she had come to for the long term, and Nora said that it meant she had to get a divorce.

*

Nora went back down to Seaford and alighted at the small station, this time more aware of the biggest platforms she had ever seen. She could not understand why it was like this. The station was nearly deserted when she arrived, and now even she was struck by station architecture: an accentuated curve carried her round from the train door on a slight angle, as if she were on the current of a strong river in flood. She felt as if she was learning to see through the eyes of another.

Only two other people got off the train and soon disappeared. They knew where they were going. She waited on a bench, hoping Herbert would not be too long. She did not know what to ask him first: where she should go, where they would live, what she should call him. Then she remembered that he didn't even know about the exchange of letters with her husband, and all that would entail.

At length he arrived. He had bought a platform ticket and he came to join her on the bench. She saw him walking towards her but stayed sitting. She wasn't sure why she was making it more difficult for him to kiss her, but obviously she was. So when he got to the bench, Herbert sat down beside her, just as if they were waiting to catch a train. Then they got up abruptly, together, and walked all the way down the platform to its far end. Now he pulled her towards him, put his arms around her shoulders, kissed her deeply, and held her still. Nora said, 'I've told him we have to get divorced.'

They walked back to their bench and then looked for a refreshment room, which was located on the other platform.

'And where's your luggage?' Herbert said, as if he had forgotten.

'Let's have something to eat and then we can talk.' Nora said.

'Why are the platforms so enormous?'

'For all the schoolboys who arrive at once, like a flood,' he explained.

They had some ham sandwiches, and some fruit loaf, and continued to sit at the table, alone together in the station refreshment rooms, talking. Then Nora came out and got on a train up to London. Herbert stayed at their table, with his head in his hands.

*

Nora was staying with different people around London. Occasionally she went home again. The seeds had germinated and her father was punctilious in watering them. He told her that Mr Westell had now uncovered more than 200 burials. He asked her if she would like to come with him to see some of the pieces in the museum, and though she was grateful to him for his quiet, unobtrusive generosity, she could not refrain from saying that she would be more interested in joining one of the suffragette meetings; she was tired of the past, and she wanted the future to change. Her father replied, quite reasonably, that it would not be so easy for him to take her to a suffragette meeting, and so they went to Letchworth to look at the Roman beakers. Nora was touched by her father's solicitude, but she still wanted to explain that she was newly awakened by the question of voting. Having only just gained representation, as a married woman with property, now she would have to forego it.

In the Museum they saw one lead tablet that would later become famous: that inscribed to the accursed Tacita. They were told that when deciphered it read *Vetus quomodo sanies significatur Tacita deficta* and that this meant: 'Tacita, hereby accursed, is labelled old like putrid gore.' Nora asked her father if Tacita didn't mean silent and her father nodded yes; they both wondered what a silent woman had done to merit such venom, and at her death as well. They took the bus back to Baldock and though her father was still marvelling at the ancient artefacts emerging from the ground, Nora was more agitated by the events that were unfolding above it. On their return Nora went to water the plants; her father to polish his tools.

*

The case went to court. It was reported that each party had had time to reflect. Nora was asked how she now felt after returning from her mother's. She said, in a strong voice, and quite clearly, that she had reflected and that she was sure that she did not love Herbert Cundall and that she loved Herbert Curtis. It was reported in several local papers, including the *Slough, Eton and Windsor Observer*, and *The Uxbridge and West Drayton Gazette*. Their accounts were almost identical, if their dates differed by a week.

*The Uxbridge and West Drayton Gazette* of 12 November 1926 printed the following:

HUSBAND'S VAIN APPEAL.—In the Divorce Court on Monday, Mr. Justice Hill granted a decree nisi to Mr. Herbert Fletcher Cundall, of Cippenham House, Cippenham, Slough, Bucks, bank clerk, for divorce from his wife Nora Patricia, on the ground of her adultery with the co-respondent, Mr. Herbert Curtis, at Seaford, Sussex. Mr. Cundall said he married in June, 1919, and lived with his wife at The Hut, Jordans, Beaconsfield. His wife had known the co-respondent from childhood. In April last she told him that Curtis had been making love to her and she was more in love with him than with witness. Witness urged her to conquer the infatuation and sent her to her mother at Baldock to think things over. When he wrote asking her to come back she replied that she had gone with Curtis to Seaford, Sussex.

## CHAPTER TWO

*Paris*

Herbert Lewis Curtis married Nora at Chelsea Registry Office in June 1927. Their only witness was Herbert's sister. They found a flat they could rent, but before they moved in, they went to France. This was the beginning of their life together. It was the first time Herbert had returned to France since the war had ended. He was uncertain about going back, but they anyway took the boat train from Victoria to Paris. Nora most wanted to go to Normandy to paint in Les Andelys, but first she wanted to go the Louvre (also because of Poussin) and the Luxembourg Museum (for the new art). And before that, she wanted to spend time in a bed with her new husband without waiting for a witness to appear.

They found a hotel not far from the station and went upstairs. It was late afternoon. They looked at each other and then looked at each other in the mirror. He stood behind her and put his arms across her chest. 'You are beautiful', he said, 'and I love you'. He had never been married and she did not know anything about his experience. Maybe, she thought, he had slept with women in France, in a hotel like this? She turned round to face him, and they kissed. They lay down together, still in their clothes, and embraced. The summer evening sun streamed through the long window and the curtains rumpled in the breeze. In the distance she could hear bells.

*

Dawn was early but she was awake. She had already spent some time contemplating the angular form beside her. She drew her fingers lightly up and down his long lean back. He turned over and pulled her to him, squashing her breasts against his body, holding her in the small of the back.

'Please', she asked, 'may I call you by your second name? My husband was called Herbert. I don't want to call you Herbert too.'

'I am your husband now', he said. 'But yes.' And went back to sleep.

They took their breakfast in the bedroom. He did not eat much and rarely talked about food, but she was interested in the salty croissant, the saltless butter, the strawberry jam. He lit a cigarette and looked at the light well and the sad geraniums across the court. He looked up at the sky and could see it was blue. 'Let's go outside', he suggested, before turning to her, moving the tray off the bed, and entering her quickly, with no ado.

And then he stayed inside her, and though he was worried he might be too heavy, she liked his weight, and in any case, he seemed lighter than her. She looked up at the ceiling, at the stucco tracery, following its lines. She held him tight. If she moved her hands she felt the sharpness of his shoulder blades, while his ribs pressed more heavily into hers. He was so thin, almost breakable. She was like an island under him. An island on a French sea, floating, suspended. They stayed like that for a long time, sleeping by turns, each perhaps afraid of breaking the spell.

*

Nora had always liked the china of Lunéville, but she discovered Lunéville was a long way by train. In any case, she could buy it in Paris. And she did. Six big plates, six small, six bowls, six cups and six saucers. It was terribly heavy, but this was a new beginning. And she wanted to be more French. They bought a cookery book, and artist's materials, and some olive oil. They went to galleries and hardware shops, they ate oysters and macaroons, they took afternoon naps, and they read to each other. Nora liked best to take off her shoes, lie down on her back, feel Lewis's arm across her waist, and to hear his breathing in her ear. She would rest her head on her crossed arms, inclined against the long pillow, and close her eyes. She would put Dublin, London, Jordans and Seaford to one side, and wallow instead in being in Paris. With Lewis.

In the quietness of the afternoon she was happy just to see the net curtain blow lazily, now and again. But before very long Lewis would sit up, light a cigarette, and take a book. Then she would ask him please to read her some poetry. Very often he did not even need to read; he thought of something he knew already, probably from his time on the French Front, when he read so few books, but the same books so often. He could recite numerous poems by heart and, while this removed him from her side, and into another place, she felt closer to him while he summoned up those words as if they were his.

It was a way in which he could be entirely himself in which she could share. She would stretch out on the bed as he walked around it, no longer concerned to bring him back to her, but ready instead to let him be. She knew little of what he was saying – though she knew the piece by Rupert Brooke with its conclusion 'And is there honey still for tea?'– and her mind was not on the poems, but on the man reciting them. She was his audience, and she made no difference. She liked that. Her presence allowed him to recite poetry, and later, when he was done, he might turn his attention to her.

*Strand on the Green*

Nora and Lewis found a house to rent in Strand on the Green. She went back to Baldock to collect the bigger of the two suitcases she had brought from Jordans, and with that, and Lewis's few bits and pieces of furniture, they set up what passed for home. Not that anyone came to visit her; the few friends she had were unsettled by the change she had effected in her life, and even her sisters were wary. She did not expect them to applaud, but she could see they kept their distance. So she focused on Lewis, when he was there, and on her work when he wasn't. Lewis could take the tube from Hammersmith to the centre, and

Nora painted, local scenes: the costermongers, the boys in the park, boating on the Serpentine, Kew.

Nora liked the boats which were tied up on the river. The way they rose and sank on the tide meant that they themselves were covered and uncovered by a coat of mud. She felt as if her paintbrush cleaned and then made them dirty again. She drew and painted them often, getting to know their colours by heart, their grubby whites and blues, never clear or clean. Like English painting itself.

In general Nora was happy enough with her situation, but when people asked her about children, then she felt embarrassed for herself, and for them. And they asked quite often, as if it was the most important thing they wished to know. They never asked her what she did, though of course if she were painting, they could see what she was doing. In any case, it was hard to answer in the negative, because that wasn't enough in itself, but no one knew what the next question should be. Whether or not it was harder to be an artist with children, she knew it was hard enough to be a wife. To be a mother too; that would have taken away all her sense of herself. Even when she was painting children playing in the park, she felt all right about looking at mothers and not being one. She was not at all sure what Lewis wanted, and whereas it was hardly surprising that her first Herbert did not become a father, this time it was perhaps surprising that the second Herbert hadn't.

Nora was older now, and perhaps any reluctance about children made itself felt? Instead she got up when she wanted to, and had her own impatience to deal with. Why did she not have an idea? Why did she not go out and draw? How much should she simply practise; how much should she seek inspiration? She made little trips, thinking about her subjects. She looked at different things; trains, bridges, the Underground station. She looked at animals as well as at children. She tried to be more adventurous; she went to see the new Whipsnade Zoo, and she visited the Gorilla House almost as soon as it was open, thinking that she might combine modern architecture and ancient beasts. She liked the circular building and the way it could open and close. It made such good sense. She thought about being modern. Did she need to find more modern things to paint? Or just paint the usual things in a different way? Or neither? Just paint honestly, what was around her, without setting it apart? To make a good picture – was that different now than before? She found no answers to any of this, and so continued to paint, in an unostentatious way, but regularly and often.

*Lloyd Square*

They moved from the river to Lloyd Square. Nora liked to be living in the centre of London. She felt that she could walk wherever she wanted, but as she wasn't a great walker, this meant going as far as Great Queen Street, to get her colours. Although their flat wasn't large, it had good enough proportions to

FROM 68 STRAND-ON-THE-GREEN     TO 3 LLOYD SQUARE W.C

please Lewis and gave her what she thought of as a
painter's view. She was captivated by the gardens
at the back of their terrace; those dirty, dark green
London gardens which had their own kind of unnat-
ural symmetry. She knew it wasn't a new idea, but
she liked the fact that she was in a little local painterly lineage. She had seen other artists' back-garden
paintings, and she knew there would be more. She
imagined all the artists at that very moment looking
out on the view at the back of their houses, a huge
panorama, shared privately.

Before long, Lewis went into partnership with
Harry Goodhart-Rendel, and he could walk to the
office in 13 Crawford Street, and generally did. The
house had just been redone in the Regency style, but
looked very modern. Its new interiors were decorated
with murals by Colin Gill, whom they had both known

when he was working as a camouflage officer. It was striking to see how it worked so well as a whole, and how Gill's paintings combined war with pleasure. Nora thought he was lucky to get a job with someone so grand, but Lewis seemed to regard it with his usual detachment. The practice was working on the new Hay's Wharf building at that time, and they were often down on the river. Goodhart-Rendel wanted to surprise people who thought of him as old-fashioned, and was pulling out all the stops to impress. Lewis had suggested that Frank Dobson might make the panels on the front of the building, and Lewis went with Nora to visit him in Chelsea to talk more about the project. Lewis and Frank had both served in the Artists Rifles regiment, and knew each other well enough. Dobson asked Nora if she would pose for him, and both Lewis and Nora were unsure what she should say. It was obvious that she was his type, they could both see that. But what did it mean, to be asked to be a model? Nora later thought she should have asked Frank if he would sit for her, that would have made it equal. It would have been the kind of thing that her friend Don Hastings would have done, but he wasn't a woman. That was the way Don made his career; he wasn't shy. He wrote to famous people and offered to sculpt their portrait. But Don wouldn't have had the problem she had in simply answering the question. She couldn't see how she could ask Dobson whether he meant in the nude. So they let the question drop. But later, when she looked at his drawings, she frequently felt she could see herself there in the heavy, handsome, long-limbed women. She also felt she could have done them herself.

Lewis often took a long time to get home, especially on spring evenings, because he was studying proportion. He was even writing about it. Architecture was all about proportion, and Lewis was happy to expound upon it, at all times and in most places. Nora had some patience, but little interest. She saw the pile of pages of his manuscript growing, and she also saw how much it repeated. But she understood that both he and Harry Goodhart-Rendel wanted to make a point about that, about continual repetition; about the value of the past: its orders, its rules, its very sameness. That the rules of the past could make the present more modern. She wondered if any such thing existed in painting. She couldn't see it clearly, whereas Harry's gift was to make it clear, at least in the moment when she was attending. She enjoyed hearing his voice on the wireless, and reading bits of his books. She wasn't concerned really to follow the argument, but felt him to be compelling. She knew he was considered slightly eccentric, but also in a way, right. Or perhaps just beyond judgement. His class and education allowed him to say things that might otherwise be contested, but Harry was allowed to say them. Probably if Lewis was to say them, no one would listen.

She knew that none of them was avant-garde, not Harry, nor Lewis, nor she; and yet, there was something modern about them too, and it was shared. It was not just the connection with France, which they all had, though that was important. In France it seemed more possible to be old-fashioned and modern at the same time. When they went to France her paintings seemed to make good sense. Maybe she was in an in-between place, which hardly existed in England? She wondered if her work could ever be considered as equivalent to that of Lewis, or Harry. Was it of any significance at all? But that wasn't the same as equivalent.

Lewis had gone down to the Côte d'Azur, to St Raphael-Valescure, where Harry had a little office. They were working on two houses and two churches in the village and along the coast. Nora envied him his trip, though he said he was not much looking forward to meeting the clients, who were rather smart English people, aristocrats or millionaires. The last ones had been the Guinness family. She knew that none of this would matter, because he would just get on with the job, while Harry had already made the connection. She was not sure if she envied Lewis this or not: jobs flowed in because of Harry's connections. She had no connections and almost no jobs. But she could do what she wanted, if she only knew what that was.

Lewis used the long train journey down to the Riviera in various ways. He read the newspapers, he checked through the Countess Russell's brief, he read John Donne, and he thought about Nora. He wondered how he would describe her if he lost her, or even if he hadn't. He decided at length to write a letter again to his sister, his old correspondent.

*Letter to Monica*

'Dear Old M

'I have not written to you for an age, but here I am alone again on a train in France, wondering whether I could describe Nora, whom you met so briefly.

'I have never drawn Nora, at least not to her knowledge, though I have tried to make little sketches from memory. But I will make a painting of her, one day, I believe. And I have never written to her, as far as I remember, or only little notes, in an illegible hand. Just scraps of paper, not worth keeping. She is full of responses, of all kinds, and I am not. But I surely could write about her, if I tried, and here I am trying. (Forgive me if this is illegible and blame the train.)

'She has just a trace of an Irish accent, which is very sensual, I think, and most evident when she is close beside me, in bed. She loves to rest on the bed lying on her back, and sometimes falls asleep in that position, completely still, like a gisant. I once took her to see the effigies in Westminster Abbey but she seemed neither convinced nor interested. I don't think she is so taken by things which are old and still, or at least not yet. I think that is a difference between us.

'At night time however, she turns over and normally falls asleep on her front. I can tell she has gone to sleep by her breathing, and she always goes ahead of me. I often envy her facility for falling asleep, but on the other hand I benefit, as I find this moment very comforting, even though it is always one-sided.

'When she wakes up she is always quick to rise, and

she washes her face over and over again with water. I tell her she is not that dirty, but she tells me it has nothing to do with dirt. She puts on her underwear in a very matter of fact way; she has never been coy in the least. I have never asked her how she behaved in this respect with her first husband; perhaps it was different, but I doubt it. I see her as constant in this respect, constant to herself.

'She has a particular predilection for making sandwiches. I don't know why, but she is always quick to suggest them, and though they are often the same, they are somehow always good. I think it is because she takes care, and she is good at imagining tastes to come in the future. I don't have that facility. Sometimes she has already thought of things in the larder that she will combine for dinner before she has even got dressed. She is also good at making her food look nice, and I can't seem to manage it. Why is that? She must care more than me. And though she is rather slapdash in the kitchen, and indeed around the house, and in her clothes, she cares in the end more than I do about arranging things well, with good colours together, and shapes.

'She is also good at finding things out about people. When she was younger, she told me, she was often maladroit, but now I think she gets it about right. People are usually quite charmed by her directness, and tell her more than I would ever find out, and more than they expect to. She asks lots of questions, but I remember the answers. She is I think more interested in seeing how far she can go. It is a bit like the way she is with cats; she doesn't really like them so much, but she wants to test their limits.

'Funnily enough, she doesn't ask me much, or at least not now. She is quite quiet, even sybilline. She is not much interested in arguments, and finds my discussions with Harry pretty tedious. But I think she has decided to let me alone because she likes not knowing me too well. Is that too recondite? I have a sense that her first husband was too ordinary, and that I have a bit of mystery. Or do I flatter myself?

'Nora is not, I think, at all flirtatious. Why do I say this? Because she is not knowing, and she is not interested in exercising any kind of power. Rather she gets deep into conversation, with all her energy, and people must be surprised. She is much more attentive than most people. But not always, not at all. If she is bored, or tired, she goes to have a lie down, and thinks nothing of it.

'There are one or two people who really fascinate her. One is Frederick Ashton, and when he comes to visit she gives him much more time than is usual. He is young, but has plenty to say. The other, whom I know less well, but whom she has got to know maybe as well as anyone could, is the Russian Ambassador. In fact she has known two: first Sokolnikov, and then Maisky. I suppose she met one because of the other, but though Maisky is quite a patron of the arts, I think she was closer to Grigori. Something, I think, to do with the fact that with him, small talk was not the easy way out. But perhaps I am being romantic, and thinking also of his fall from grace.

'I haven't said anything about her painting, I see now, on reading what I've written. But I like it, and she is working hard.

'Trust your writing is going well.

'Your affectionate (Herb you used to call me, but now) Lewis!'

*Sainte Geneviève*

They went to Paris together again. And to the cathedral towns they could get to by train. Lewis liked to draw the architecture and Nora the parks. Sometimes they sat together facing different ways. Some of the cathedrals were in ruins after the war, and Lewis did not draw them then. He had seen them before, because during the war he had used all his leave to travel round France. He knew the buildings of France better than he knew his own family. But now he looked carefully, as far as he could, studying the structures with greater attention for what they could give him. In Paris, the church of Saint-Etienne-du-Mont, with its complicated inter-crossing Renaissance interior, was of special fascination. Each time they went back he drew a different part – the screen, the stairs, the pulpit – in painstaking detail. While he did that, Nora sometimes visited the remains of Sainte Geneviève, thinking about having a mountain named in your honour. Nora was not religious, but she liked the story. And the name, too, was pretty, if pronounced by the French.

She read in the leaflet how Geneviève had rallied the Parisians to defend their city, after Attila the Hun had razed Metz and Reims. It seemed all too contemporary, and all over again. Geneviève was the *defensor civitatis*. Nora tried to remember how to say this to tell Lewis. Geneviève later surrendered Paris to Clovis, King of the Franks, on condition that he converted. Paris became his capital in 508, and he and Geneviève both died only a few years later. Her relics were often taken across to Notre Dame, in grand processions of thanks or imploration. What was left of her reliquary after the Revolution was placed in Saint-Étienne-du-Mont.

In 1933 Lewis and Nora went to Paris before Easter and stayed in the Hotel de la Paix which Nora had discovered among the streets of the Montagne Sainte-Geneviève, while Lewis was drawing in the Saint-Étienne-du-Mont church. She liked its position in a little impasse, and its narrow height, and for no very good reason thought of it as theirs. She could walk along to the Jardin des Plantes to draw the big cats, if she wanted, or stay in their room, waiting for his return. Sometimes he came back later than she expected, sometimes earlier. She liked it best when he came in while she was resting, daydreaming, lying on her back. He would stroke her eyebrows, straighten out her hair, and unbutton her blouse. He would kiss her breasts, silently, and for a long time. Then they would take off their clothes and make love, more and more slowly, as the light fell and the lamps came on outside. He would endlessly trace the curves of her ample body and try to commit their soft shapes to memory. But he never drew her, only buildings. She, on the other hand, often drew him.

That summer Nora felt strangely enervated. Going up the stairs at home, and especially at the Underground, seemed unusually tiring. She went to the doctor. He examined her, inside and out. The doctor asked her if she had considered the possibility that she might be pregnant. Nora was forty-three years old and she was pregnant.

On Saint Geneviève's day, 1934, Nora gave birth to a son, born by Caesarean section. He was given three names, one of them being the name of the mountain where he had been conceived, and of the saint who had preserved Paris from the Huns. They only told him about two. Adam Sebastian.

## CHAPTER THREE

*Adam*

The baby was plump and had blue eyes and blond curls. He was like a cherub who had arrived from another place; not of their making. When he was just a few weeks old Nora painted him from above, wrapped in white linen, like swaddling clothes. It looked ethereal, quite like a Renaissance painting. When, a little later in the Spring, Nora took him out in a pram, people seemed to treat her as if she were a nurse, whom they ignored, all their attention focused on this compelling little force.

The baby was voracious. The baby had a huge voice. The baby had tears which were big and sugary, and sat on its cheeks like diamonds, until the baby savoured them with experimental interest. The baby was hungry and liked to eat all kinds of foodstuffs. The baby was thirsty, and took anything to drink. The baby explored the skirting boards, the edges of the mats, the ridges in the floorboards, the castor wheels, the wires, in short, everything. The baby refused nothing, was frightened of nothing. It even liked to be frightened; loud noises made it exclaim and gurgle.

For months Nora stopped painting altogether, but then she tied the baby into a chair and painted him, very well. She was pleased to discover that one of her best portraits was that of her son. It had scale, and

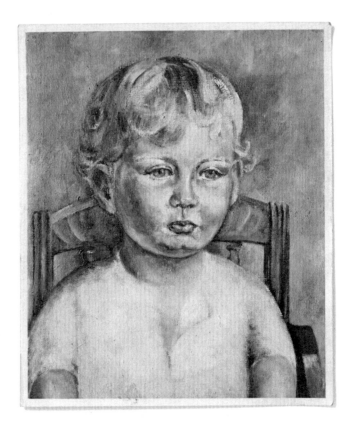

force, and an absolute rightness. He looked like a prince, or even like a little king-in-waiting.

When the baby could walk they found a young girl from Denmark who came to help. Her name was Inge. The name for her was an 'au pair', and she did indeed seem to be like their equal, taking Adam for daily walks along the river. She told him the names for the birds in Danish. He was not able to reciprocate. She was fascinated by the Underground, and when she was not looking after him, she went to the city centre. She was looking forward to the coronation of Edward VIII in May and in the event was able instead to catch a glimpse of the newly crowned George VI.

While Inge was out with Adam, Nora was painting hard. She was also recuperating and framing the paintings she already had. This new focus came from the fact that she had been invited to have a show in the Bloomsbury Gallery, and had to make up for lost time. Lewis told her to go and have a look at the galleries and make herself more aware of what was being shown. But Nora felt like doing the opposite; staying away from the centre. Avoiding talk. Maybe this was because she had read Harry's review of Herbert Read's book on the Unit One group and saw how cynical he was about what the artists said. She saw that even though he quite liked their work, he didn't like the way they talked about it. She asked Lewis why he thought Harry was so sarcastic about artists talking, especially when he himself loved to talk? Did he think that artists should just make art? Lewis thought that might be partly the reason. He also thought that Herbert Read probably represented something to which Harry was viscerally opposed. Maybe Harry wanted always to be the commentator, yes that was probably so, but he also liked a certain eclecticism, so the Unit One position was probably much too rigid for him (and he was an architect, and not an artist, even if he chose to comment on artists).

Nora thought about this for some time. In the end she came to the conclusion that Unit One was probably just too serious for Harry, and perhaps for most people.

Nora had already seen in *The Times* a letter from Paul Nash in which he said that his Unit One group would build a hard defence, a compact wall against the tide. By tide he seemed to mean nature. He thought most English artists had been blinded by nature. He thought English art was weak because it had no structure, no purpose. Nora recognized the problem this represented. Even if she was just painting landscapes and people, she knew herself how difficult it was to be taken seriously, and especially with a landscape. How could you transform something that most people thought was a picture to hang over a mantelpiece into something that was seen as work? Maybe it would be easier if it did not look like anything. People would tell her she was good at capturing a scene, or a face, but almost no one could go beyond that. And she herself found it nearly as hard. Or perhaps even harder. She sympathized with those artists who tried to say something, and to make that something more important. But did that something need to be in disguise?

*Chalcot Road*

They had to move again, and found a nice double storey flat in Primrose Hill. Nora could now walk to the zoo and pursue the animal studies she had started before their marriage. She went a few times, sitting in front of the same cage where Lewis had surprised her with his declaration. Somehow now she achieved greater concentration, and while Inge took Adam to the park, Nora was able not only to begin new work, but also to understand better what she had done before. She knew she had not to worry too much about critics and groupings, even if she too wanted to be taken seriously. She thought she would choose to show the painting of three cows; two brown and one white. She brought it out from the stack and took a long look. She believed it was a good piece, but how could she ever say anything about what she had been thinking when she painted it? And she didn't mean that it meant anything terribly private. In fact, what it meant was something public, but she couldn't express it well. She could say the painting was anchored at its centre by a tree which separated the two brown cows, each facing away from its trunk. It was very balanced picture, focused on this quiet crossing. The white cow was in the foreground. The painting was not about cows, of course. So what was it about? About light? Colour? Or was it in fact about the pleasing shape of cows as they grazed, something sculptural, and enduring? So it was about cows? She remembered mixing those milky greens of early summer, before nature had turned a richer yellow. She remembered the way the field tipped down and how beyond it a bank of older trees was still slightly wrapped in morning mist. But it wasn't about the

weather. Nor was it about her, or about Lewis, or
about their time in Normandy, though she remembered it well, and with affection. She remembered
setting off, leaving him in the hotel. She had been the
first in the breakfast room, and had not lingered. She
had had her café au lait, some baguette and apricot
jam, and had left the village swiftly. When she left
the track she stepped onto a dewy field and her feet
quickly got wet. She found a place with less grass and
set up her easel and canvas. It was blank. In front of
her were layers upon layers of details, which she was
to simplify into a painting, on a size 20 canvas.

Over the next three mornings she had done this,
leaving Lewis in the hotel working on his drawings,
and completing, to her satisfaction, something that
became a painting. The painting's time was morning,
the dew and the mist of breakfast time, and the
shadows of noon. The cows never moved, they were
not caught grazing, but made to graze, for ever. The
tree was an old tree, with young foliage, newly opened
and as yet undefined. It would hang softly in the
lavender sky when Nora decided to paint no more, to
let this painting be this painting, with its mixture of
definition and the undefined. It meant nothing, but it
was a painting, a painting that worked, and would go
on working.

Now, in London, wondering about what selection
to make, she saw very clearly that her paintings had
no stories. Did this mean they had no meaning? No
message? She would not be able to talk about them
to Herbert Read; they would not fit into any defined

structure. Would it be wrong of her to think that was what was good about them? That by refusing to have meaning, their message was that they were about themselves? If Nora had been a reader, or a musician, she might have made comparisons across the art forms. But she did not read books, nor play music. What she did was to make sophisticated paintings in a simple way, or to make simple paintings, in a sophisticated way. She did not articulate this, but neither would she think such a judgement was wholly wrong. This is what she wanted to talk to someone about.

Landscape had, without her quite realizing, become something essential. It had taken this long for her to be attuned to its importance, to want to render it effectively, not because it was Normandy, or any other place specifically, but because it was landscape. This had nothing to do with topography, but everything to do with understanding how we manage and what helps. And then she saw that landscape did a good job of disguising itself, wrapping something essential in so many trees. It re-attached itself to us when it was well painted. Then we remembered the painting, more than nature, but we found the painting again once we were back in nature. She found this hard to put into words, even to herself.

*Bloomsbury Gallery*

The Bloomsbury Gallery had recently shown attractive works by well-placed English artists, as well as

a promotional show for a society promoting rela-
tions between the people of the Commonwealth and
the USSR. Knowing of this range, Nora was more
than a little uncertain about what note to strike. Left-
wing and right-wing, traditional and modern, these
confused her, and not because she was stupid. She
reckoned, but was not completely sure, that Ambassador Maisky was most probably behind the invitation.
That meant perhaps that the left-wing was more relevant than the right-wing, but she knew perfectly well
that he knew what her paintings were like. Perhaps
their modest realism was in fact exactly right? Maybe
she did not need to worry who was behind this invitation and what it was about. Even if Maisky was
Russian, he was well-liked. He was always about the
place, and buying good things too. And so what if
he, or the gallery, showed Russian art; that wasn't a
problem for her. And when they had encountered
each other at openings, she had liked him.

She decided to show some wood engravings as well
as paintings, knowing that these would likely sell, and
because she wanted to earn some money. They had
however to be framed, and Lewis and Nora tried to use
old frames whenever possible, and to do it themselves.
They hung the show together, with Nora standing back
to get the distances right, and the men putting in the
hooks and nails. She had a good eye, and could judge
whether the frames were hanging straight better than
they could, even though they had a spirit level.

She had chosen 18 paintings and eight engravings.
The paintings represented her short life with Lewis;

their trips outside Paris – some down in the Côte d'Azur, painted while he was working – and their life in London; some on the Thames, some in the parks of London, and some from the first-floor windows of terraced houses. Looking at them together she saw that they were devoid of people, and suddenly felt her eyes looking into loneliness. Bridges, boats, boathouses; fountains, squares, gateposts; green-houses, gardens, paths; all uninhabited. Of course, when she was painting them, they weren't. But now, in the gallery, they spoke of motifs; different kinds of places, but not of different kinds of people.

At the opening people asked her where exactly the places were, whether she preferred to paint in France, and, sometimes, even, whether she painted 'en plein air' or 'sur le motif'. Nobody asked her what they meant, which was as much an irritation as a relief. Nobody asked what they were about, and she herself had only just begun to develop a way of answering a question which nobody yet had asked. There was one review, or rather, a paragraph; part of the 'London round-up'.

> *Mrs Curtis is showing a number of very competent landscapes, including 'Boats at Le Havre', 'The Cactus House at Kew' and 'Les Andelys'. A subdued matte palette and very competent handling of the brush combine to produce paintings of structure, with an almost architectonic mastery of composition.*

(None were sold.)

*Monica*

Lewis's sister Monica had published a book and they were invited to a small dinner to mark the occasion. Normally she lived in Geneva, where she was working on international affairs, and was coming back to London specially. They were all going to meet at Victor Gollancz's publishing house in Henrietta Street and go out in Covent Garden. When they got there they discovered that other books were being celebrated too; some just fiction, some political, and some a mixture, like Monica's.

Monica did not appear to be the most important of Victor's authors, but they could see how she fitted in. Victor made a little speech as he toasted her and the others, and reminded his guests of why these books mattered; they asked their readers not to drift into unconsciousness, allowing the aftermath of the last war to befuddle them into a kind of feigned insouciance. They must not confuse what was happening in Germany with what was happening in Russia, and what might even be happening here at home. With this he gave a specific nod to Monica, who nodded back, in her slightly grim way.

Nora found Monica a bit alien, but she was impressed by the evening. If she understood correctly, Victor even tried to encourage his best writers to use their powers as storytellers to warn the British public of what might happen, if they were not careful. As she and Lewis went home on the Underground she asked him if he thought there would be another war. Lewis thought not. Nora calculated that he would be too old to fight. Lewis dismissed this observation, explaining that warfare was not the great threat which Gollancz had in mind, but rather brainwashing. If she read Monica's book, she would see more clearly. It was about the rise of dictatorships, and how this happened, almost without anyone noticing. Monica had been interested in the nature of power for a long time but he had not expected her to write a novel about it; normally she was editing other people's speeches.

Nora took the book out of its brown paper wrapping and looked again at its virulent yellow dustjacket. It told her, boldly stated, in big letters, that it was a powerful and beautiful novel and that it was '1st and foremost an extremely good story; 2nd an important sociological and political study; 3rdly, had brilliant qualities of a purely descriptive kind'. Then she took off the dust jacket and looked inside to find a plain black book with a tiny title on the spine which looked very forbidding. They had arrived at their station. Nora gave the book back to Lewis who folded up the brown paper and returned the yellow dust jacket to the book.

When they got home they found a parcel inside. In it there were three copies of *The Studio* magazine, featuring Nora's drawings from the zoo. Lewis was pleased with this but Nora felt dissatisfied, feeling the difference between the artistic range of Victor Gollancz's authors and her little drawings. Lewis told her that the two things were not comparable, and that anyway Monica's novel would have no impact, being

By *Monica Curtis*

# LANDSLIDE

A remarkably powerful and beautiful novel. Indeed, one is embarrassed by the very profusion of its merits.

1st and foremost, it is an extremely good story: 2nd, it is important as a sociological & political study: 3rdly, it has brilliant qualities of a purely descriptive kind.

insufficiently clear. As Nora had not read the book, she would not understand what he meant, but in his view it was far too elliptical. Although Nora knew he was probably right, it suited her to belittle the importance of her sketches, even if she knew they were good. But she cherished a line that the reviewer had added about her exhibition, even if it was too late to make any difference.

### *Hatchlands*

Lewis and Nora were invited down to Harry's country estate, Hatchlands. They caught the train at Waterloo and walked from Clandon station. It took them nearly an hour. Neither was a quick walker; Lewis smoked too much and Nora was a little heavy. But they were accustomed to walking and expressly told Harry not to collect them. In fact they enjoyed the exercise, especially in advance of what they knew would be a substantial lunch.

Nora told Lewis she was looking forward to seeing the paintings again; it was nice to see a house with proper paintings. Lewis said he wanted to revisit the Adam interiors. Halfway along Nora suggested they have a rest. They sat on the parapet of a little bridge and Nora laid her head on Lewis's shoulder. He held her hand. It was nice to have a quiet moment together before the social activity of the country house. Nora knew too that much of the conversation would be architectural, and provocative, and that she wouldn't be able to keep up, or rather, didn't really care, one way or the other, about the return of whatever. She saw more clearly now that Lewis's repeated visits to Saint-Étienne-du-Mont tied in with something both men wanted to prove. About not discarding the past, while believing in changing the future. A plea for diversity, but also for knowledge.

When they arrived at the house they were taken through to have a drink, and introduced to a number of people whose names Nora at once forgot. She edged away from the group and looked around her. She was interested to see these grand paintings so much at home in their surroundings. She thought about her own work, and that it, too, settled into its environment. She did not think of her work or her home as humble, but rather as appropriate. Her paintings had a browny greenness quite different to the azure roseate tones of the paintings here, but one that suited their more modest destinations, so different from this grand country house. Nora thought about the difference between a portrait and a painting, and how they are judged. What was more important, to satisfy those who knew the sitter, or those who didn't? To make a good portrait, or to make a good painting? She painted people of no public significance whatsoever, even people whose names were of so little significance they would soon be forgotten. (Though perhaps that little girl she had just painted would turn out to be somebody, she had a feeling.) Here, on the other hand, there were politicians, engineers, statesmen, and Rendels after Rendels. Nora had never quite understood the Rendel connection, which was apparently not really Harry's name, but an addition.

*

'Come, dearest Nora! Don't abandon us altogether.' said her host. 'Wouldn't you like a spot of lunch?' Nora demurred and followed the group into the dining room. They were seated and a *vichyssoise* was served. Nora looked up at the intricate ceiling, painted in a green similar to that of the soup, and picked out in white, with in-filling of pale coral pink and primrose yellow. The walls were pale green too, and the silky carpet, like a sheep's underbelly, tufty but smooth, was pale yellow and blue. She slipped off one of her shoes to enjoy the carpet's texture, which she remembered from before. The soup had ice cubes in it, and sent a chill down her throat. She wished she could just lie down now on one of the settees next door and allow the conversation simply to act as a background to her reverie.

But more courses came, more conversation, more wine. Lewis seemed animated. After a coffee in the drawing room she suggested to Harry that they might take a stroll in the garden, and he agreed at once, taking her by the arm and leading the way. He knew less about plants than he did about buildings and music, but he was still quite well informed. She was impressed. They walked down to the pond and Harry asked her about Adam. She explained that they had found a Danish au pair girl which allowed her to manage to do some painting. Harry did not ask about the painting, but he was interested in the idea of an 'au pair', and wondered where that term came from. He had never heard it used in France. Was Adam more like her or Lewis? She thought he looked more like her. But who did he take after in terms of brains? 'Ah,' she sighed, 'someone else must be the judge of that.'

Harry's chauffeur drove them to the station and they sat in the waiting room for a while. Nora thought back to the time they met in Seaford.

'It must be so different to have all those things around you,' she murmured to Lewis.

'Yes, but they are not all his you know. They mostly come from the Rendel family. He had to take that name because his grandfather insisted.'

'Who was he?'

'Lord Rendel.'

'But still, that house must have been with them for such a long time.'

'No, I don't think it has. I think Lord Rendel bought it after he became successful.'

'But still, Harry has so many things. He even has a village. And more villages in France!'

'Yes, but it all comes from the female side.'

They boarded the train back to London. They arrived when dusk was falling. Nora felt heavy; she had eaten and drunk a little too much, but it had not made her content. Indeed, the opposite; she felt a lingering spell of dissatisfaction that she couldn't explain to Lewis. Or perhaps even to herself. She decided to have a lie-down and try and dispel her mood in sleep. She half undressed and lay down, partly drawing the curtains. She could hear the trains arriving at and departing from Euston station. She imagined being on one of them, perhaps in a sleeping car, perhaps with Lewis.

### Hyde Park Gate

Victor Gollancz arranged for Ivan Maisky to visit Jacob Epstein's studio and Maisky commissioned Epstein to sculpt a portrait. It wasn't a very grand

portrait, or particularly original, but it was by Epstein.
Maisky had been in London since 1932 and he could
see there was no better artist to ask. Moreover, he was
rather fascinated by Epstein's persona, and saw him
as a fellow traveller. He had not expected Epstein to
be so cross about everything, especially art, but he
hadn't regretted his decision. He had already been to
18 Hyde Park Gate four times, and today was supposed to be the penultimate sitting.

Maisky could easily have been driven across the
park from Kensington Palace Gardens by his chauffeur, but he preferred to walk. He liked to look at the
Albert Memorial and consider this curious people
who mocked him for his country's reverence towards
their leaders. He liked sometimes to stop off at the
newly-opened Serpentine tea rooms and order something outlandish, like Battenburg cake, or Empire
biscuits. He enjoyed the tea, and as he looked at the
counter, and the waitresses, he could see why English
painters were drawn to these scenes. He was thinking of that painting he had just seen by Coldstream
of the Café Conte, with various artists looking at the
cakes. So British, he thought. Who could imagine
that in Russia, never mind France? Artists looking at
cakes! Coldstream was one of those painstaking real-
ists. He was said to demand more than a year's worth
of weekly sittings. Lucky that Epstein didn't have the
patience for that. Although, he must admit, he had
hoped for something a little more inventive.

However, it wasn't finished yet. Maybe something
would happen. Maisky completed his journey and

rang the bell. When the door opened a number of black cats ran out. Epstein called from the first floor, in his big American accent, 'Come on up'. Maisky proceeded up the stairs and pushed open the studio door. He saw Epstein drawing a prostrate cat, which promptly jumped off the table. Epstein explained that he was resting after working on one of his carvings. Maisky knew that these were enormous, and uncommissioned. He presumed his little bust was one of many which was helping to pay for their execution. Epstein quickly picked up his usual rant against the British establishment, the art world, its critics, the museums, and above all the Royal Academy. He judged the Academy to be a kind of iron-clad cartel which controlled almost everything artistic in England, and with uninspiring results. Being American gave him the right to see this objectively. As Maisky settled into the model's chair, and as Epstein unwrapped his clay, Maisky thought about academies and academicians, about state patronage, and official portraiture. He was pleased he had enough money to commission his own bust, but also wondered if this was why it looked so terribly modest.

The bust was cast over the summer, and Maisky was surprised to discover that there were five examples. He felt a little uneasy about this. Who, he wondered, might buy his image, and why? He took the first copy in the edition, and it was delivered in the diplomatic car a little later. As it happened, one of the first artists to see it was Nora, whom he had met at the New English Art Club, and who occasionally called. He liked Nora for two reasons, that he knew of. She looked slightly Russian, and she spoke clearly, without giggling. He hadn't thought so much about what she said, but in fact he liked that too.

As the bronze was still in its crate, but with the lid and the front face removed, Nora had a chance to comment. She said, and he knew that she would, that it was awfully small. Very frontal, which made it rather oriental, she thought. 'Perhaps you might have it patinated gold? That would give it a bit more presence. Quite like, though. Quite like.' Maisky had been thinking a lot about the relationship between what one looked like and what one was like. To what extent did a man's features shape his character? Or vice versa? He had even been collecting caricatures and sharing them with Francis Klingender, who was going to make a book about cartoons which would, he hoped, be sympathetic to the communist cause. He wouldn't say that Epstein had caricatured him, but he had disembodied him so completely that his was just a little head balancing on a block. Maisky knew, from looking at portraiture, that sculpted heads could become tremendously emblematic. He had to admit he was disappointed. Perhaps he hadn't paid enough attention to the business of being portrayed? But there again, perhaps he had no aura to portray?

Nora had got no further than the hall. The maid advanced to take her coat, just as Maisky's wife came into the hall. Nora prepared herself to say hello, but was cut short as Mrs Maisky closed the front door behind her, excusing herself as she did. Nora noticed

another new arrival at the end of the hall; a bust by
Barbara Hepworth. Maisky told her he had bought it
from the artist, who hadn't liked it, saying it was an
unimportant early work. Nora asked who it was, and
Maisky looked in a tray of papers and found a note;
'Mrs Nora Robbins'. 'Nora, is it so very common?',
joked Maisky. 'Come and have a sherry. How is your
little boy and your frightening husband?' 'They are
well', she replied, 'but I want to talk about myself,
and my work. I know you must be busy, but do you
have a little time? Can you listen?'

Maisky ushered Nora into the sitting room and
encouraged her to sit on the window seat, allowing
him to be closer, and the light of the London square
to fall upon the table between them. Nora was not at
all sure what she was going to say, or quite why she
had felt impelled to come here. Maisky offered her
a cigarette and lit it, clumsily, but with good grace.
'Nora, my dear', he said, 'how can I help you?' Nora
thought of everything she might say, but wouldn't.
She smiled, with her broad full lips stretching back
to reveal strong even teeth. When she smiled she
looked more Russian. Why had she come here to try
and establish what it was she wanted to say? Did she
need the help of a diplomat?

'Mr Maisky... Ivan. I do not expect that you can
help me. I just wanted to try and put into words
something of my situation. If you will forgive me,
I will try. You can be my witness. Some years ago,
as you know, I married my husband. It was my
second marriage, and I went through a very awkward

situation to get to that point. It wasn't so very easy, but I was sure. I left my husband, and I also left the community we had started together, based on Quaker practice. It was a good place, and he and I had had expectations. Now I am living with my new husband, whom I do love. There is no question of that. And he is happy for me to paint. He encourages me, in fact. Buying me paints, and things I need. And we take trips together, and we both paint. But I feel, quite distinctly, that for both of us, it is only seen as a pastime, a diversion...'

Maisky looked at Nora's face to see if she had stopped talking, and suggested she might explain to him what exactly a pastime was. Nora knew that he did not mean that it passed the time. He meant, how seriously? In fact, it was a good question.

'For him, it is what he needs as an extra. A pastime for when he is not working. But for me, it is my work. Or should be. I want to take it like that, and I want him to as well. I want him, and me, to take my work more seriously. In fact I want it to be seen as work. Just work. I want my work to be my centre.'

'As much as him?', asked the Ambassador. 'And your child?'

'Yes. As much as them.' She replied, finishing her cigarette and looking out on the greenery of the square, up to the tops of the plane trees, and above them, to the light blue sky. 'Or even more.'

'And is it your problem, or his?', asked Maisky, evenly.

'I think... I think it is shared,' said Nora. 'It is

natural enough that his work seems more like work, and mine more like leisure. I feel that too. But I need to be more serious, and so does he. About my work.'

'Yes,' said Maisky. 'This is a shared problem. We are all guilty. And it is not a question of success, but of perception. You must try harder.'

Nora felt the scene around her. Their dark figures against the luminous square; the works around them which betokened English art; the huge marble chimneypiece. She smelt the cut flowers and the tobacco. She heard the occasional motor car and the sweeper's brush on the pavement. She looked at Maisky's dark eyes, set within his small head, and wondered about the shape of his skull. Her eyes met his and they smiled, together. He reached slightly forward, put his small pointed hand on her arm, and said, briskly, as he rose, 'You are right, or rather, we are all wrong.'

*Art worlds*

Nora was taken by Ivan Maisky to a number of exhibitions that summer. She wasn't sure quite why, or what he expected from her. Partly, she felt, it was his interest in understanding the local context. Although he was better connected, she could narrate the local scene quite deftly, in ways that he seemed to appreciate. She could tell him about the places in London where people painted, or about the landscapes. Maisky had no comprehension of where Cornwall or Cumberland were, for example, or what they meant.

He was eager for information, and she was able to supply only a small part of what he wanted.

After they had made a few trips together, and they had settled into a way of arriving, greeting, looking round, commenting and leaving, she understood that Maisky was agitated by events at home, and that this was a kind of light relief. Many of the gallerists knew him, and whereas she could have looked round anonymously, he had to exchange pleasantries. Whereas this would be a burden for her, he seemed perfectly ready, and sometimes it meant that they saw behind the scenes or learnt interesting snippets of information. All in all, Maisky took it seriously enough and Nora wondered why, in comparison to what was happening in Russia. He had talked about art in the USSR and she had been impressed by the scale and ambition of the schemes, which made what was happening in Britain seem rather paltry. Maisky said that he liked the human scale of what was happening in Britain and that some artists, like Epstein, had grand plans. He liked too to know who was who, who supported who, and how the circles of patronage worked. Nora was fascinated to see him at work, or at play, and understood her innocence. But knowing how little she had to give him in this respect, made her wonder again why she was here.

She was however able to tell him that they could go to see Goodhart-Rendel's bust while it was being sculpted by Dora Gordine. She was interested to see it, but also keen to accept the offer of a lift out to Kingston Hill. She had assumed that Maisky might know

Dora, given the Russian connection, but apparently not. They were both impressed by the studio house, but Nora soon tired of Dora's continual chatter. She wondered, if money were no object, what kind of house she might have built for herself, or what kind of house Lewis might have built for them both. As far as she was concerned, Dora was more like one of Goodhart-Rendel's rich clients than like her. Bessboroughs, Rothschilds, old money, new money, what difference? She wasn't comfortable either with Dora's exotic subject matter, heads of native chiefs and the bodies of near-naked dancers, mounted like trophies on cabinets of imperial wood. She was embarrassed enough, heaven knows, with herself for painting the costermongers in the market at Hammersmith, and only dared to do so after weeks of buying their goods.

They went too to the Royal Academy Summer Exhibition. Charles Cundall had been made an Associate that year and so they seemed to find his work in every room. He had been painting all over the country – London, the South Coast, the West Country – and Spain. She had to admit that there was something very clever in the way he caught the game between Chelsea and Arsenal in a huge bowl of lime green pitch. It was grand but also everyday. 'Spectacular and vernacular at the same time', suggested Maisky. 'Perhaps he is in keeping with the times?' She saw that Charles was good at bringing you into the crowd while allowing you to take in the panorama. She supposed that this comfortable mastery of the scene, a

kind of knowing familiarity, was what had got him
elected. She supposed that was an accolade. She
could see how well he had done, and how she hadn't.
She wondered where his brother was now, and what
it would have been like still to be with him. She wondered if they would have come together to a dinner
here to celebrate Charles.

Funnily enough it was Maisky who told her that
there had been a lot of talk about the Royal Academy
not supporting Epstein, and that some well known
Academicians had resigned in sympathy. Mr Sickert,
who had only just been elected, had just as promptly
resigned. It made Nora see more clearly that sides
could be taken, and also that she had not realised
this. She compared Cundall's pleasing compositions,
with their sense of complete space, with the pictures
she knew of by Sickert; flat, dry, shallow, uneven: all
in all, puzzling. She wondered how painting equated
with morality. Maisky suggested they walk down to
the Strand and take a look at Epstein's statues, the
ones that had caused the fuss. They saw the emaciated figures high up on the Rhodesian Embassy,
figures that had become headless caryatids. Maisky
explained that the first attacks were religious: priests
and old women saying the sculpture was a dangerous
moral influence. When the Embassy had bought the
building they said the carving was dangerous because
the stone was loose, and might fall. 'Dangerous in
every way', he winced. 'Moral and physical.' Nora
thought about who needed protection. The artist or
the work? Or the public! Why should art set a good

example? How could stone be immoral? Maisky pointed out that these carvings were not new. They were thirty years old now, but this new scandal had turned them back into modern art.

## Religion

Harry had converted. He had become Roman Catholic. It was the talk of the office, and of the town. Lewis and Nora discussed what it meant, to become a Roman Catholic, in the 1930s. Was it a modern gesture? Could it in fact be seen as radical, rather than as reactionary? For Lewis, however, it primarily meant even more work, especially after Harry met Abbot Upson, a Benedictine monk with ideas that only matched Harry's in grandeur. One day they all motored down to Gloucestershire to look at the site where the Abbot wanted to develop a monastery for 100 monks. They had fun in the car getting their tongues around its name, and all the different local variations of its pronounciation. Nora said Prinage; Harry said Prinidge; Lewis said Prinnish.

Prinknash Park included a large old house which had been made over to the Order just before the death of the owner, who had himself only recently converted. The monks had been anxious about the grandson honouring his intentions, but he did, and the monks became the owners of the estate. On arrival Harry introduced Lewis and Nora to Wilfrid Upson who welcomed them in a very civil manner and invited them in for lunch. However he had to explain that were other areas where Nora would not be allowed, and she had to wait behind when he took the men in. She and Lewis began to see how much the brother-hood mattered to Harry and how he was becoming part of it. After lunch they walked round the site and both Harry and Lewis made little sketches of the sloped setting. When they were doing this the Abbot told Nora that he felt no sense of urgency. Even if the world was to go to war, as everyone thought would happen, he and his monks would continue to build the abbey, just as if it were a medieval building site, with masons learning their craft together from each other, over generations. He knew it might take a very long time. He joked with Nora that it might make a good subject for an epic film. Nora had no idea how serious he was.

Harry and Lewis began work on the project almost at once, and they had already designed, and drawn, huge plans based both on their journeys around France, but also on their recent projects at home. Harry was well placed to think of building up a whole community, modern and old at the same time; it was what he had been doing on his family estate and in the village of Clandon. The Abbey was to be some-thing of a composite of all they had learnt and all they had seen. It was at once terribly rational and com-pletely mad. It seemed as if they were trying to put everything into this scheme, as if it were their last chance.

War was indeed declared and Harry went off,

leaving Lewis in charge of the office. Upson dropped by quite regularly, always keen to see Lewis's drawings, and even to show Lewis his. He seemed to show no qualms about the enormous size of the project, but Lewis saw the drawings as being more like those of an artist than of an architect. He thought the plan was impossible, and thought too that quite possibly Harry was perfectly well aware of this.

## CHAPTER FOUR

*Catkin Cottage*

In the autumn of 1939 Lewis found them a house where they would be safer than in London. It was in a small village in Bedfordshire. Lewis had identified it when he was working on the church there. Lewis could get there quite easily, and so could continue working in London during the week. He was busier than ever, even now, because Harry had gone away to join his Brigade, and Lewis was to take care of the partnership. Even if there were few new commissions, there were still a number of churches to be finished off. Harry had launched any number of grand plans; Lewis had to see that they were finished off, even now in the midst of war. And there was Prinknash, in another league altogether. Lewis would miss Harry's presence, but his absence would make life simpler.

In High Wycombe they discovered that they could buy furniture that was made locally. Neither had realised that they were in the heart of the industry here. Soon they would discover the men responsible – the bodgers – in the woods around them. Lewis bought some new chairs, as well as some second-hand pieces, and made some tables from kits. He established Nora and Adam in the house and, though he missed them, was glad to think they were out of London. Nora was acquiescent, but pained, nonetheless.

The weeks were long and uneventful. Nora and

Adam gardened together, and Adam was good at helping her, and good at creating his own little patch. They shared a taste for the ground, enjoying the feel of breaking up the crystalline soil in their hands, sticking their fingers in the furrows, making little castellated earthworks which could gather the water for newly planted vegetables. Kensworth was very quiet. Sometimes Nora liked this, but not always. On bad days – especially when Adam was having lessons with the teacher he now shared with five other children – it reminded her of Jordans, which she found unsettling.

She decided she should paint herself as a kind of life-affirming gesture. She thought carefully about how to go about it. She chose a simple chair, and set it on a striped rug. It was a bit more stable than the other chairs, which were a motley group. She thought about the clothes she liked, but also about how she wanted to look. She thought it would be nice to dress in red, and to look poised. She decided against arm-chairs and mirrors and flowers, and instead to be honest about what she was doing: painting a self-portrait of the artist, in a more or less empty room, to which she had no especial attachment. She manoeu-vred her long mirror into position, sat down and crossed her legs. She knew already that this position would get uncomfortable, but she liked it. It gave her some assurance.

She went upstairs to look at her clothes, which were not many, and in poor condition. She put on her vermilion dress, which had a loose collar, and put on her only pair of silk stockings and polished her shoes. She also did her hair up, in two chignons, and thought that these preparations might become wearisome if the painting took a long time.

She painted herself when Adam was busy, pottering round the garden, making mud-pies, talking to the birds. He seemed to have lots of things on the go, and she didn't need to worry about him too much. But if it rained, or he wanted attention, he came in to play and she set him on a mat in one corner of the room, sometimes breaking off from her portrait to sketch him instead.

When she finished herself she put the painting on a stool and thought about what she had achieved. A quite flattering painting of a woman of indeterminate age in a room that was so empty that it seemed strange. It wasn't at all comfortable in the Bloomsbury kind of way. It wasn't an 'English interior', and in this respect was quite truthful. But nor was it obviously a portrait of an artist, as she didn't represent herself painting, and none of her tools was evident. So in this respect it was untruthful. And did she feel better about herself now? And her situation? She thought it looked like a painting of a woman who had no real place, but wanted to prove she was here, nonetheless.

*

Adam's teacher told her young charges about life under the sea. None of the children had ever seen the sea, but the teacher told them it was full of all kinds of natural life. When Adam got home he asked Nora to draw sea creatures and she made a big drawing with jellyfish at the top, starfish in the middle, and anemones at the bottom. He did not know if she was making it up or whether it was real, and when he asked her to draw more underwater animals, at other times, she refused. Instead she painted his teacher.

Painting some of the few acquaintances she had made in the village was a helpful way of passing the time, and she hoped it was also good for her work. But the days went slowly, and she often envied Lewis in London, and resented her confinement in the country. She thought that the only approach she could usefully take was to immerse herself more thoroughly.

After Adam had had his breakfast she would try to make herself sit down and have a piece of toast. If it was sunny she would pull her chair into the sun and extend this moment, which she enjoyed, if she remembered to do it. She would try not to move, but just eat slowly, putting little bits of honey along the crusts. She would have loved a cup of coffee, but had to make do with tea. Then she would go upstairs and try to make a new combination out of her meagre wardrobe, and maybe put her hair up differently. She would walk round the corner to take Adam to his classes, and usually meet the postman on the way. In the shop she tried her very best to be friendly, but it never seemed to be enough. How long, she wondered, before she could ask to paint the strange-looking Miss Campbell, with her big jaw, frizzy fringe, and odd colour combinations? Better question: how long would it be before someone asked her to paint them? An age, Nora thought, as she knew no one here, and most people had no money, and those who did, would hardly think even to exchange the time of day with her. She needed to think differently. Could she make more of her enforced stay by painting what was happening? Not portraits, or landscapes, or still lifes, but life?

*The bodgers*

Adam had quickly become fascinated by the bodgers. Nora too loved looking at these woodland scenes. The bodgers usually worked in the beech woods which covered the area, and had little wooden shacks in which to work and to house their tools. There they transformed the green wood into chair legs, turning them on a lathe. Now, when Adam got bored, he asked to visit the bodgers, and he loved to play around the copses and the huts. Nora would often have a cup of tea with the Deans, or with Reg, and Adam would be given a biscuit.

'Let's visit the bodgers!' he cried, in the late Indian summer they were experiencing that year. Nora took her paints and he got onto his tricycle. They set off, a little more laden down than they would have liked. The weather was uncertain, but they knew the splendid canopy of trees would shelter them. They made their way along the lanes, passing only a few cottages and some animals. Everything was quiet, except for the squeaking of the tricycle.

They did not know which of the bodgers would be working where; sometimes they moved section, or worked at home. Nora liked to find a scene where there was work to be done over the next few hours, or even days. She knew the men well enough to be able to check with them where it was worth settling down. They had to go a little further than usual today, and they got a little tired. The weather became more sultry, and they had nothing to drink. Nora was almost fifty years old; the boy on the tricycle five.

The trees leaned in over them, descending the steep hill like an army with banners. Their smooth trunks rose up straight, but then their branches bent inwards over the road. The canopy of leaves rustled only very slightly; the breeze was hardly palpable. Then a little more, and suddenly the leaves were tossing and turning, as if reaching out for help, unsure where to turn. There was a rumble of thunder. Nora counted aloud; the boy wondered why. One, two, three, four, five; the lightning struck. The rain began.

Nora tried to protect her sketchbook, her paints and her brushes. She tried to put the sketches inside her blouse. She got caught up with the brushes and lost concentration. Lightning struck again and Adam careered down the hill on his tricycle, coming off at a rut near the bottom. Nora dropped her things and ran down the hill. She picked him up and let the blood running from his knees merge with the rains which were now amassing heavily, like sheets of water. She had never been afraid of thunderstorms before.

She wanted to find shelter, but most to find some-where to take care of Adam. The nearest hut belonged to a man she did not know well. Nonetheless, she thought he would probably know who she was and let her in. She need hardly have wondered; he was standing at the edge of the hut, smoking a pipe.

Seeing what had happened to the child, and the state of the woman, he was prompt to offer shelter. They stepped inside and Nora asked if it was possible to have hot water. The man said no, but he had a bottle of iodine. He used Nora's handkerchief to dab it onto Adam's knee. Adam flinched and nearly cried, but didn't. Nora looked imploringly into the man's eyes and he touched her cheek for the briefest of moments. She did not move, and neither did he. Neither did Adam. The rain went on pouring. Some of the smaller twigs and branches came down, as did the beechnuts. The hut was not quite waterproof, but it made all the difference. They sat inside, on stools, looking on at the green wetness. Adam was sorry that the thunder was abating; he thought he might never hear it again. Nora and the man – 'What is your name, I'm so sorry?' – told him that he would. Then the man touched her lips. With his fingers. Nora felt both anxious and content. The heavy rain was tranquillising. Her son was alright. She was happy enough to be out of harm's way. She was, perhaps, even happy. She sat on the little stool, her child on her lap, her cheek against his. Nora and Adam looked out at the rain, and right beside them was a man they did not know.

Nora and Adam returned home, and stayed at home more and more. On occasion, and especially when she could not sleep, Nora thought about that moment, wondering quite what it meant. She had gone back to the hut some weeks later, but no one was there. Very often at night she would come downstairs, heavily but softly, to sit on the easy chair by the fire, with its embers still alight. She would let her mind wander, and invariably it wandered back to that hut, and she recast its scene in her mind, making it last longer than it actually had.

Then she might light a candle and look around her, at the muted colours and into the shadows. It was too dark to read, but she might pour a little sloe gin, and be happy to contemplate the space in which she sat. The wooden floor and doors. The uneven walls, painted in a blueish distemper. The inset shelves of books, almost all Lewis's. The heavy pot-plants, her painted cushion covers, the old American wall clock which had belonged to some member of Lewis's family. She thought about ten years ago, her frustration then, with her first Herbert, and her frustration now, with her second.

She would savour this contemplative moment, alone in the semi-darkness, and maybe pour another little glass. Her eyes could manage the headlines of the papers, but not much more: 'British Thrust in Desert', 'Why has Rommel retired?', 'Soap rationing starts today', and so on. Sometimes she would put another fir cone on the fire and see it come briefly to life. At that moment she felt drawn to its activity, shared between her and the fireplace. After this moment of absorption, she would blow out the candle and thread her way up the short staircase, feeling its awkward treads and clumsy curve with her soles and fingers. She would get into bed, hoping the map that marked the limits of sleep would have given way to unknown territory.

On a foray into the woods a year or so later Nora retraced her steps to the hut, wondering what might have become of it. It seemed clear that it had been abandoned, and everything had been cleared out. No signs of human habitation remained, other than the hut itself. She stood inside for a long moment, imagining again the storm, and the sensation of Adam on her knee, and the man at her side. Before leaving she turned around, and then saw a handkerchief, stained, as if with blood, nailed up in the back corner. Its continued presence here made her feel curious, and all the sadder.

That autumn, they began to hear the bombs dropping on London. Then they watched. Like a huge bonfire party, between Christmas and New Year, they watched the flames on the invisible horizon. Adam gathered up all the excitement he remembered from when he and Nora had watched the Crystal Palace burn down in London. They had stood on the riverbank at home and watched the fire burn in Sydenham, miles south of the Thames. Many thousands of people had watched the Crystal Palace burn down, from all over London, and the memory had stayed with Adam vividly. He had wanted to see more of that. And now he was seeing it again. Nora had to plead with him to stop looking. She could not bear to watch, and Adam only wanted more.

On occasion Nora cooked from *Plats nouveaux!,* the cookery book she and Lewis had bought together. She liked the menus, twelve for each season. The recipes she used were the ones Lewis had helped translate. She liked to make *tarte aux tomates, carottes aux raisins*, and, just now and again, and when she could, *curry de lapin*. She could no longer make *Oranges caramelisées*, or *Crème Caramel*. There were no oranges, and there was almost no sugar. They had bought the book in Paris, but she would never visit Paris again. Within ten years, there were no more bodgers.

*In the woods, writes Nora*

'This morning I woke early and I gave Adam his breakfast. He was already playing with his little farm animals. I folded up the washing and thought about the day, how to make it work.

'I want to convey the way the landscape pulls me in. I want to make a well-built painting, but I also want to communicate the feeling here of being inside the landscape. I paint and paint, but only seem to begin to approach that state of being in the trees. I want somehow to be as good as the bodgers, like them, totally with the landscape. I don't see them as being in the view, or as a subject matter. Instead they are, to me, on a level with the trees themselves. Part of the same plane. I like these scenes but they are more than scenes. These people represent a way of working which is completely equal to the place where they are, and that is what I want.

'Lewis will come here on Sunday, I think, and then I can paint him. He has come to be more accepting of my using him and I like the way he is adapting to the landscape, even if he still wears his suit. He has recently learnt to scythe the grass. He has to do more and more manual work, as there is no one else to do it. It is as if we are going backwards in time, but I don't even mind. I just mind that the war never ends.

'I can no longer go and look at paintings in the museums, but I used to do that a lot, and the books are mostly here. I don't need that anymore, anyway. Now I must try to be inside my subject, not outside it. The deep green lanes here are quite different to what I used to do, looking for something to paint. Now I am inside it, and I need to express that, without being whimsical.

'In the church in Missenden there is a plaque to the minister which was designed by Eric Gill. There is another plaque by him in Little Hampden. It is nice to find something well done, and modern, in the countryside. I thought about paying a visit to meet him, but was unsure in the end. I couldn't imagine what I could say. What interests me, in fact? Not really the art, but rather the possibility of the art. Here he is. Living so close-by, in a village no bigger than this one, and yet an artist. Buried in the countryside, but a public artist. Making commissions, for here and for London. Writing, publishing, pronouncing.'

*

'Eric Gill has died, so I can't visit him now. I saw an obituary in the newspaper. He did a lot in fifty-eight years; only ten years older than me. People round here say that he kept very close; it's hard to know really what they mean. I can hardly imagine making so much work, especially away from home, on such a scale. He has found a way of using an old craft for a modern expression. How does he make his carvings look quite modern? How does that come about? They do the same thing as carved tablets always did. Is it just that they really are new? Clean new stone? Is it just their simplicity after the Victorians? But then we can do the same in painting; just being plain might be enough?

'On my way home from the church I met Ted Dean. He told me he had bid successfully for a good bit of woodland. I congratulated him; I think I like him best of all the bodgers round here, but then many have gone off to war, and only the older ones are left. Ted is good to me; he helps in various ways. He lays the mouse traps, and drops off manure for the garden.

'Adam is really helpful in the garden now. He can put the manure in his little wheelbarrow and take it to the spots I identify. We give the rhubarb and the roses a good feed. Adam always asks so many questions, and often I find myself passing on something I have just been told by Ted. But Adam remembers it much better than I do. I think he is so much alone that there is somehow a gap in his brain which gets filled with facts. He is beginning to read quite well, but most of all he likes to plant seeds. We have a whole army of pots, and he remembers all their names. He seems clumsy but in fact he never squashes anything.

'The woods are getting quieter now, as the bodgers thin out. Some are in the forces, but others have simply got too old. I feel as if my paintings are catching something historic, which is odd for paintings made outdoors in front of the subject matter itself. I think Ted knows this too, somehow we share a mood of melancholy. He tells me about the birds, and the trees, but it is like something that is over.

'We had to move, but I didn't mind. We go from one plant name to another (Catkin to Vine). The new house has woods front and back. I was sorry to lose some of the work we did in the garden, but I can always make a new one. Lewis found some people to help move the furniture and it was quite jolly. Even Adam helped move his toys.'

### A Visit

One day in July Nora got a telegram. MUST BID FAREWELL. PROPOSE WED c. 3 p.m. IM

On Wednesday Nora felt rather nervous, not knowing what to expect. She had not seen Maisky since she had come to the country four years earlier. She made herself a little sandwich and ate it with a cup of tea. She then made sure things looked clean and cut some roses and euphorbia and put them in a vase. She decided, to fill in the time, to make some bread. She weighed out a pound of flour, a teaspoonful of sugar, and of salt, and creamed her yeast. She mixed it together in her big beige bowl, dampened a tea-towel, put it over the bowl, and set the bowl to one side, out of any draughts.

Not long after she had done this, a noticeably large car drew up outside the house. As the chauffeur opened its rear door, she opened the door of the cottage. Maisky stepped forward briskly with a parcel wrapped in brown paper. He waved the chauffeur off, saying something that was incomprehensible to his hostess.

'Well, here you are at last. In the English countryside.'

'I have been in the countryside before. But not with you. This is what is novel for me.'

'Of course, I know you go to Hampshire. You are right. As usual.'

They smiled at each other, equals in the discussion.

'Let me see what you are doing.'

She showed him her easel, with a painting of Adam surrounded by his toys. The tricycle lay behind him, with some building blocks and farm animals scattered in the mid-distance. Adam was absorbed with a pig. It was quite a big painting, almost life-size. Everything looked a bit dirty, but then, looking round, Maisky could see that everything looked a bit dirty too. On the walls he could see various drawings of trees. Some were filled in with colour, others not. The trees looked very English to his eye, whereas Adam looked as if he could have been a little boy in a Russian painting.

'May I see more?'

'Of course.'

She showed him the vegetable beds, the beans coming along, the beetroot, potatoes, spinach. Nora had some more unusual things too: scorzonera, kohlrabi, but she soon saw that all vegetables were essentially equal for Ivan. They admired together the sweet peas and roses, and Nora lamented the loss of the lavender, lupins and delphiniums, all the blues. Maisky, who looked so different here, at once completely out of place and completely at home, told her not to worry. She could rest assured that she would see them next year. Alas, he would not. He had no choice but to return to Russia, and did not know what faced him there.

Back inside he asked her to show him round. She said there was not much to see; the front room, the kitchen, the larder.

'And upstairs?' he asked.

'Yes, if you wish', she answered.

*

When they came down the bread had risen over the top of the bowl and was collapsing down its sides. The tea towel was sticking to the dough as she peeled it off.

'No use crying over spilt milk', said Maisky. 'That is your expression isn't it?'

'More or less', said Nora.

They both heard the car draw up on the roughly made-up road. She looked at him as if in fright.

'No, you won't see me again. That is why I came today. I hope you will be well, in whichever way you wish. I am pleased to have seen you.'

Then Maisky turned to leave, contriving to be at once formal and intimate, inclining his head, and kissing her hand. He left at once. Nora stood at the door as Maisky disappeared into the car. The chauffeur barely acknowledged her as he moved round and took his seat. The car left.

Nora pulled the dough out of the bowl and beat it down. And again, and again, and again. She pushed it back into a ball, put it in the tin, and covered it over with a clean tea towel. She sat down by the window and closed her eyes. When she opened them she saw the parcel. Inside was a book entitled *Art from the USSR*. She would not see Lewis for two days. She would never see Maisky again.

*

When Lewis came back, on Friday afternoon, he asked her about the book. He could see that it was published in London, but he was sure Nora hadn't been to London to buy it. No, she began, wondering how to continue.

'Ivan Maisky came here.'

Lewis was incredulous.

'Maisky came here? The Soviet Ambassador to the Court of St James's came to see you, here? Why?'

'Because he wanted to say goodbye.'

'He wanted to say goodbye to you?'

'Yes.'

'He came all the way out here to say goodbye to you?'

'Yes. He has been recalled.'

'Has he been here before?'

'No, of course not.'

Adam was upstairs, but he heard the plates fly, and he remembered the sound of the heavy china breaking.

'And he won't come again.'

'No, he won't come again. He will probably be dead before very long.'

'Don't be ridiculous.'

'I'm not. That is what usually happens. And I might as well die too.'

When the child came down to see what had happened, the kitchen floor was covered in pieces of white china, white with tiny pink, blue and green flecks. He gathered up the bigger pieces, but soon saw it was a hopeless task, and let them lie.

*Distance*

Lewis went back to London and stayed there for longer periods. He was intensely involved in drawing up Goodhart-Rendel's schemes. The Prinknash drawings had been published before the war broke out, but now that Harry was away, Lewis was intent on mastering the finer details of Roman Catholic doctrine, although he was not even a believer. And Lewis spent days, weeks and months rendering Harry's visions in precise hard lines, making even the most unlikely compositions seem real. Despite his attention to detail, Lewis had a presentiment that these projects could never happen. They were almost literally like castles in the air, rising loftily and ethereally above their terrestrial sites. Sometimes some friend or acquaintance wrote to Nora in the country, having seen something by her in one of the scattering of exhibitions that was still mounted even in war-time London. Lewis had taken one or two of her works down with him, and very occasionally she would make the journey with Adam, especially to hear one of the concerts organized by Myra Hess at the National Gallery. Although they were surrounded by empty frames, to listen to the musicians in the gallery itself was somehow still important. The letters that arrived at home were quite touching, even encouraging.

*Darling Nora, I was entranced by your latest work. How you find the courage and the time to continue painting I just don't know. It must be hard when you sell so little. But I must say, I was really impressed by what you are doing. It is fully as good as anything I see in London. I hope you won't be deterred. These deep green scenes of your walks in and around your house are memorable; I carry their image with me.*

*Dearest Nora, congratulations on your new paintings. I think the move to an English location has done you good. Not that your French paintings were bad, far from it. But now I feel a sense of your being rooted, and these new pictures of your son, your husband and the people around benefit, from a new familiarity, the kind of informality of an inhabited landscape.*

*Dear Mrs C., I hope you won't mind my writing to you unexpectedly. But I wanted to reassure of you of my deep respect for your work. I do very much know how lonely it is to be an artist, especially when you really are alone most of the time. But what you are doing is wonderful, I do think. It is so apparently modest, but goes a long way. Without rhetoric, you find something that is truly painterly. I hope you will not be discouraged, and will allow me to visit you again.*

And the scattering of reviews was also positive:

*N.C. has, this year, surprised us with her contribution. These small paintings of dense woodland reveal small figures at work amongst the greenery. These people, known locally as 'bodgers', have come to fascinate the artist. Her rich creamy palette, suggesting new growth and fresh foliage, or the green-wood itself, does justice to the scene of quiet industry.* (None were sold.)

*N.C contributes domestic scenes largely dominated by her son. We see him at play, with his toys around him. We see him asleep. We see him gardening, carrying a small pail. Charming scenes dominated by a mother's love.* (None were sold.)

Nora was quiet, reflexive, for longer periods. She dwelt on what had happened, and on how it should not have. She dwelt on those last words to Lewis and on what she meant by them. She decided to try and paint this out of her, and, unusually, went into her studio to think about it. Her studio was hardly worthy of the name, being really a kind of back parlour, which had neither carpet nor curtains. She sat on her stool, in front of the empty easel, and, once again, considered her position.

When Lewis next came back he asked her what she had been doing and she said she had been painting, something different. Not just bigger, but different. She did not offer to show it to him, so he did not pursue his question. Instead he went outside and began to scythe the grass.

After Lewis had left for London, Adam asked Nora if he could see what she had done in the studio. Nora said it wasn't finished yet, and anyway, she preferred not. This was the first time she had said this to Adam, and he felt a little chill between them. Or a moment of growing up, together. One day he came back from his lessons and walked into the hall. Seeing the studio door open he went in to greet Nora, who was not there. On the easel was a large painting with white lilies at the front, and behind, a big gravestone. On the stone was written just one word: his mother's name.

### Christmas presents ('Tout comprendre')

Lewis came home for the Christmas holiday and told Nora he had been reading *War and Peace*. For Christmas he gave her a little pendant which he said had a connection. It was very delicate (really too delicate for her physique) and she was not sure if he had had it already or had found it recently. It had an inscription in French which she wondered about, but did not ask further because she was embarrassed. She also felt, more or less, that he wanted to close this chapter of uncertainty. As neither of them wanted to say any more about it, at least out loud, Nora did not put the necklace on, even thinking that it might not fit. Instead she put it by the bed and took his hand, which she put on her cheek. They just briefly caught each other's eye, and then Nora sat down on the bed and put her arms round her husband. His waistcoat buttons pressed into her cheek.

For Christmas Nora procured a duck and she and Adam covered the house in greenery. So much that Lewis was a bit shocked; he said it was like camouflage. They wondered if that was a reference to something that had happened to him in the Great War, but doubted they would ever know. Anyhow, the duck was good and the house looked beautiful. It was very tiring for Nora though, and her legs felt as if they were made of lead. After Christmas Adam and Lewis took down the greenery and removed it to the bottom of the garden. Lewis went back to London.

After Lewis had returned to work, Nora looked in the dictionary to see if she could find his quotation. She couldn't, and she didn't want to ask him what it meant. She knew what the individual words meant – all to understand all to forgive – but couldn't understand the saying. Did he understand? If he understood, would he forgive? Had he already forgiven? In any case she didn't want even to start to try and explain the Maisky episode, because she did not know if she even could. Had she known what she was doing, and did she even want to? Nora was conscious of burying something she'd rather not consider... There was, she imagined, some kind of clever connection which Lewis had worked out in his head and didn't even need to explain. The pendant was very lovely though.

Adam and Nora stayed together in the quiet house, quietly. Sometimes they looked at plant lists, and discussed what they might order for the spring. Adam ticked off some names, and made a separate list of orders. Nora lay back in the chair, her head on the curved brow, her hand on Adam's arm. She would ask him to get a stool for her feet and he would sit on another beside her. She might put her hands through his hair, which he liked, and they would sit there until it was completely dark, and then Nora would ask Adam to light the lamp. They were still waiting to be connected to the mains. Nora thought a lot about Lewis's gift while she was alone. It was like an impossible riddle. She began to wonder if it were a challenge. She thought perhaps he had had it made specially, so as to let her know that if she told him everything, then he would forgive her. But would he have given her such a lovely a gift if he had not? She knew he had not understood everything, and she could not imagine that he thought he had. Was she forgiven or not? This was maddening. If he knew everything, would he forgive her? But perhaps understanding is not the same as knowing? Maybe he understood enough to forgive her. She decided to try and let this explanation suffice, but the words continued to ring in her head: *Tout comprendre, c'est tout pardonner.*

*

Sometimes when Adam came home from school now he found his mother upstairs in the bedroom, lying on her bed. At first he was worried, but he became used to her taking rests, and was ready to go up and read his books beside her. She had no interest in his homework, or even sympathy, but sometimes a thrush or a blackbird would break the silence of the late winter evening, and they would look up together, and smile. The song was hanging in the space between day and night. They talked about how to describe it; Nora thought it was like the light between two curtains, Adam a strip of silver. Or a thin waterfall.

Later his mother would say, 'What about some food?', and would rise, slowly, putting on her shoes again and going down behind him, telling him in advance what he might do. She sat on a stool and they considered the options: Nora made suggestions and Adam carried them out. Sometimes he could go into the garden and even in the dark knew how to bring back some vegetables, all muddy and cold. They ate simple things at the kitchen table, potatoes and spinach, beetroots and chard, but with a bit of bacon, or even root ginger, to cheer them up. They enjoyed their meals together, and talked about new ways to cook.

Sometimes, however, Nora preferred to stay in the bedroom, and asked Adam to bring her something to eat. He did his best to make it look interesting, arranging a tray with some bread and sardines, putting black pepper and parsley on top. He would pick a Christmas rose to make the tray prettier, and take it upstairs, knowing that then his mother would suggest that he tell them a story. He would put another rug on the bed, draw the curtains for her, and attempt to make a story good enough to make them both forget where they were, for a moment, and transport them to a place with hippogryphs and unicorns, a story as good as one in the *Blue Fairy Book*.

## Without Adam

'We decided we should send Adam away to school. Lewis took the decision, he is right, I am sure, but I dread his departure. But here he sees so few people and I am no company for a young boy. He is so full of life and he tires me out. Often I have to rest all afternoon just to summon up the energy to make him supper. When I am resting, I think about painting a lot. I go into my head and into the green lanes. How will I ever do them justice?

'I lie down and close my eyes and picture the views from the roads around here, and how they would work in a rectangle. I have painted so many imaginary pictures. And the ones which I have already begun jostle for my attention, crowding in front of my eyes. I have to somehow steer my attention between them until it comes to rest on the right picture to paint. Then I allow my eyes to pull back, and I sketch it out, and drain it of colour, so as to get the shapes. If Adam is at school, will I paint better?

'I took my paints along the lane and settled there on a tree trunk which I know about. I set up my easel and brought out my canvas. I have been working on it now for three mornings. I nearly close my eyes and let the trees come close. The big cedar tree which grows on the green dominates with its trunk, but I can't see much of its foliage. The gorse is what I see most, but above me there is a forest of green. I know all these trees but I have to forget that I know their shapes. I have to be inside these trees, and not just looking at them. I painted slowly, but well, I think. When I got back to the house Adam was thirsty. When I poured him a glass of cordial, I dropped the bottle. He seemed so shocked. Maybe it was the first time he saw me making a mistake.

'At the weekend Lewis will bring some friends from London for lunch. Adam seems quite excited. Finding the food might be a bit difficult, but I think we can get a chicken. I asked Adam to go and ask the farmers if they could put one aside for us. When he came back he had some eggs and some bread. That was sweet of them, and I don't know what I can give them in return. A painting!

'Lunch was nice, though I wish I had someone to help. Lewis told stories and even recited poetry, like he used to. He did his favourite thing: walking round the table to the beat of Lars Porsena. Just like all those years ago; Macaulay's *Lays of Rome* in the train to Seaford. I think his work is going well. With mine, I feel I was getting somewhere but that now I have lost my control. I can't quite put my finger on it. Even my writing looks less shapely.

'Today Adam went off to school. It was a black day for me. I made Lewis organise it all. I only packed Adam's trunk and held him, for longer than he wanted. But he was good about it; he said he had planted hyacinths and he thought they would be ready for Christmas when he came home. I shall miss his busy-ness so much, he is always trying things out. I sat in the wicker chair and looked into his eyes, which are not as bright as Lewis's, but still very blue. He has a round round face and lovely curly hair. I pinched his cheeks and kissed them. He gave me a hug, like he always does. I don't suppose he realises how alone I shall be.

'After he had gone, I decided to make some tea. I found it so hard to lift the kettle. I was afraid I would drop it so I waited till Lewis came back. He held my hands, all stained with soil and paint, and stroked them. We sat in front of the fire for some time and we said nothing. I asked him to make the tea, and he asked me why I hadn't. Not up to it, I explained.

'Lewis went back to London today. I tried to do some drawing but it was no good. I looked at Adam's hyacinths under the sink and sent him a wish. Mrs Pegham came by to deliver some milk and I asked her to help me change the beds. She seemed surprised but happy to help. If you can come again I would be so grateful, I said to her. I didn't tell Lewis I was planning to get help, but I think it is sensible. And I like Mrs Pegham. Maybe also I could try to paint her.

'I made an omelette for lunch and I dropped the bowl. I managed to clear it up, but it was a waste of the eggs which Dorothy brought. Everything is quiet, with no son, and no husband. I didn't want to draw or read. The garden can take care of itself for now. I put on the wireless. The surrender ceremony with Japan was signed on an American battleship. War is over. Again.

'I went upstairs and sat on the wicker chair. I took down my hair and brushed it, then I put it up again. I looked at the garden, at all the work Adam and I did. Round the window the vines are curling, a little dry now. Lewis is probably making drawings of a church, in his hard precise line. Adam is, I hope, making some new friends. I lay on the bed and thought about these years. I cannot summon the energy to really start painting again. The bodgers too have gone. I miss their presence, though I hardly go there now. Was it the war which made them go? Or just modern times?

'The walls of this room are very uneven, and covered in limewash. There are three paintings hanging, one on each wall. 'Kensington Ponds', with children playing with their boats. I can almost hear them now, their shrieks and exaggerated roars of triumph. The boats at Le Havre, a quite ambitious painting, of big dirty working boats, pulled up on the beach. Why did I paint that? To be more French than the French? But it is not like any French painter. And 'Snow at Kensworth', where we used to live. So many homes, so many places to paint. It helps you to get to know the place, but does it help to get to know yourself? Or your art? But the painting is good. Maybe it is true I was thinking of Sisley, in Louveciennes, but my painting is strong nonetheless. It has that same envelope of milky colours, a kind of almost smothering quality of material and light which heavy snow can bring. I can look at this painting often. Luckily. I don't think I can ever paint so well again.

'Christmas 1945. Adam came home and wanted everything to be like it was last year. I told him to pick laurel and holly and that his father could put it up. He wanted to know if his hyacinths were ready and I told him to go and look in the garden shed. I had not been down there for a while. He came back with two pots, one with white heads appearing and the other with blue. He seemed restored by this, and so was I. Their scent soon began to fill the house. I wanted the flowers to last forever, or at least until after he returned to school.'

## CHAPTER FIVE

*Lewis again*

One winter morning, early in the new year, Lewis received a packet of the letters he had written to his sister from the front during the Great War. Lewis had been in France for four whole years, but the only letter that could be dated now was the one about the first Christmas, when he had been sick, and thus relieved from front-line duty in the trenches. Lewis gave the letters to Nora to read, which she did, intently. She had always wondered about his time there.

The letters were not about the war; they told Nora nothing of what she had wanted to know. They were also all very similar: the reader, the writer, one viewer. Brought together in a scene that later, it seemed, Nora would paint. But the letters were not addressed to Nora, even if her work seemed to respond so directly to the images they summoned up. They were all addressed to Monica, whom Nora hardly knew, though she knew she was pretty well educated, and quite successful. She had been to Cambridge and to Oxford, and was making a decent career writing reports on international affairs. Nora had never read the book she had written, though she had been to its launch, and remembered it as a kind of science fiction. Had it been a warning, and one that was right in the end? Perhaps she was a little scared of this sister, who had moreover seemed to share so much with Lewis at that time.

She thought she should read that yellow book. It was on the very top shelf and just getting to it was a challenge. Now she remembered it was published by Victor Gollancz, who had also known Maisky. It was much easier to read than she expected, and she wondered why she had never read it before. Perhaps because it was written just when Adam was born? She remembered that Lewis had not been very impressed, or had thought it would make no difference. What difference could a book make anyway?

In any case, reading it now made Monica seem much more human and less frightening than Nora had imagined. She talked about friendship, and love, and marriage, all in quite a realistic and accurate way, even if she herself had never married. But the backdrop to this close-knit English group was a dictator called Leo Steele, a Mussolini-type whose new state forced the English into exile in the Alps, where they got to know the villagers. It ended with an unlikely scene in which the dictator is found conversing with the group's father figure at midnight outside their mountain refuge. Nothing more happens. Nora wondered why Monica had written it. It was so carefully done, and well written, but with no kind of ending. It seemed, in her eyes, to be as much a love story as a warning. She thought she remembered Lewis saying that nobody would take it seriously, but Monica was proved right, thought Nora. She must have seen what Hitler was about before most of us had.

Lewis did not spend much time on the packet of letters, but Nora poured over them. She loved the way they repeated themselves. She had begun by making an effort to put them in order, to match the letters to the envelopes, but soon realised it would be difficult, or impossible, and in any case, would make little difference. These letters gave no sense of evolution, or even of time itself. They were almost all the same letter, set even in the same season. And now she could see too a link with Monica's book, which had a similar bond with nature – and also had an eye on the horizon – and was even interlaced with lines of poems. They all seemed, in their different ways, to be painting the same view. After she had read them several times, she put them back in the envelope Lewis had brought them in, carefully, but in no particular order. She found herself repeatedly returning to the images they conjured up.

*I have found a very nice field of buttercups*
*about ten minutes from where I work and when*
*the sun shines and I'm off duty I go there to lie*
*amongst them. Beyond the field there is a row*
*of young poplars and beyond that the low blue*
*hills and in the field are dark chestnut cows*
*with purple shadows. The cows have a knack of*
*arranging themselves in the most picturesque*
*positions. All these things are a great solace.*
*Try and imagine again two green woodpeckers*
*flying amongst the apple trees of an immense*
*sunbathed orchard. Can you see them with*
*their backs shining like burnished brass in the*
*sunshine? As you watch them you must fancy*

*that your eye just catches the long grass below
full of speedwell and buttercups and a starry
white flower very like edelweiss, and in your
ears there is a mighty chorus of bullfinches,
larks, yellowhammers and every bird that sings.*

*Today I walked out into a vast brown field and
watched a man ploughing with a white horse
and a boy behind him sowing seed, all against
a pale blue afternoon sky with a dusty sort of
yellow sinking among a line of trees.*

*Today being May Day I went down a long white
road towards some low wooded hills. Presently I
found a green field dotted with trees so I laid me
down in the sun and went to sleep. There was a
magpie in the field and he flew into a dark blue
wood. The air is quite clear here and the woods
are mixed darkest blue and lightest green. Along
the white roads peasants pass – girls in black
with lace collars and men in ornate corduroy
suits and braided caps. Everything is bright and
clean. Sometimes you see a squadron of cavalry
pass.*

She loved the way the letters summoned up a canvas,
with its low horizon lines, paler foreground and
distant banks of deeper colours, the visual contrasts,
and along with that, the sounds. She was sure she
could paint these views. In fact she knew she had
already painted them. How long it had taken her to

get to this point, to a glimmer of understanding. Such long gaps between the letters, the book, the paintings. Two wars alongside. She wanted to paint Lewis as if he was in his letter. Maybe she would put herself beside him. If she could summon the strength.

*

Lewis could see how fascinated she was, and she could see his curiosity. She thought she ought to try and put this into words. She told him that she thought the letters were miraculous. Miraculous that he had written them, that they had arrived, that they still existed, that she had read them now, over three decades later. But most miraculous, she told him was that they proved her wrong, in the best of ways.

'What do you mean?', he asked.

'I was always expecting them to be all about the war, and they are all not about the war.'

'I couldn't do it; not just not allowed, but incapable.'

'But they are beautiful.'

'You think so?'

'Absolutely.'

'I think they just show that I wasn't up to it.'

'I always thought the shadow hanging over you was the ugliness of the war, but these are simply beautiful.'

'They are just simple evasions.'

'But they seem to me to be real, really about you and what you saw. A real way of managing.'

'Yes, that is true.'

'I feel less afraid of you now.'

'Nora, my darling, that is ridiculous. Why should you be afraid of me?'

'Because of what you went through and never talked about. But now I see how you held on to something beautiful.'

'I always thought it quite hopeless.'

Now this couple, who had found their way of getting along, through a mixture of affection and respect, looked at each other almost sentimentally. They were equals in their reticence, their quietnesses, all that went unspoken, but they had chosen each other and not regretted it.

'But no, that is quite wrong. It was amazing. It still is. All that beauty in this time, it's extraordinary.'

Lewis reached out for her, pulled her up, kissed her and held her close. She laughed briefly. He sighed. She sighed. He laughed a little. And then together, they laughed and laughed, and held each other closer, surprised and delighted by something that had overcome them both, together, at the same time.

'Oh my sweetheart.'

She felt as if these letters were meant for her. As if Lewis had intended to find the artist who would paint them. Who already was painting them. Or it. For all the letters were one letter, and there was one scene, and it was described in all the letters she had singled out, and it was there, too, on the first page of Monica's book. It was France, and it was England. It was that real landscape which had comforted them, and that real landscape which had been lost, and that landscape which they became so expert at summoning up, as a first and last resort. A real hallucination.

*Can you imagine a great wide field stretching
so far that the trees at the further end are just
a blue gray shadow, and can you see that field
thick with dandelions in bloom from end to end
and everything quivering in brilliant sunshine...*

*It is yellow, and then blue, and then brown, with
some purple. It is field, and then wood, and then
sky. It is road, and tree, and sky. It is flat, and
then vertical, and then the airy envelope. Birds
sing there. Soldiers do not fight there. People find
words for it, they remember it, they paint it, they
look at it. It is peace.*

*Losing Nora*

Adam went to stay with his parents after he finished school and before he went to university. Then he realised how much his mother's health had declined. Within a short time Lewis had arranged for him to go to Rome, on a study tour of its buildings and museums. Adam went, with some excitement, but as much uncertainty. He could discern that Lewis wanted him to go abroad, and he was not entirely sure that he should. By the time he returned, and before the summer was out, Nora had been taken to hospital. She had fallen and broken her hip.

Then Lewis suggested Adam should take up a sport, and he found himself learning to dive. In between times he was doing field trips with the Geological Association; they met at different London stations and went out to the city's boundaries to analyse the sedimentary layers of the London Basin. It was clear to them both that such activity was a way of not dwelling on what was closer at hand. Nonetheless it was odd how Adam was delving deeper into the obscure regions of the greater London Basin, while his mother struggled on a hospital bed.

Nora asked Adam to bring her sketchbooks and some pen and ink, and while in her hospital bed she tried to make sketches of the nurses. Even when they stayed still for her a few extra moments, she was too slow. She made them look big and ugly, when they were small and pretty. They were so dexterous and she had become so clumsy. She was worried that they would mind being portrayed so badly but no one seemed really to mind about anything. Except Adam and Lewis.

Nora wondered about what she was leaving behind her apart from them. She had even only recently discovered that all the paintings she had left behind in London in 1939 were damaged and had been destroyed. Whether or not they were any good, they no longer existed. So, what she had, were those few paintings made before the war which had survived only because they had been framed, and those which she had painted in Kensworth and Missenden. She would leave behind two husbands. Though she had kept with her no material trace of the first Herbert, she knew he was still alive. The second Herbert seemed unready to talk about what was happening, and was even trying to keep Adam away from the hospital. She would leave them nothing of any value; nothing which talked of this strange adventure with Lewis which had set them apart from so many of their family and friends, except some paintings, almost all of them paintings of the English countryside. She too had found in it her safe haven.

Lewis thought more and more about France while Nora was in hospital. He thought about the time they had spent there together, and how, unless, and even when, they were making love, it was always ringed by sadness. France was still, for him, a war zone. Even though he had only been on the front line for the first year before he was relocated to the cartography division, he never felt free from its imagery. He could draw, he could write letters home, he could read, but none of these activities helped him to edit it out. He wrote regularly to his sister, trying to be honest, and failing. He wanted to tell her something of what he had experienced, but found it impossible to be truthful, and to know how to tell the truth. The fact that it was not allowed was probably a relief. But neither could he write about other things, except, the picture, half real and half imagined, of the place beyond war. He tried to push out the ugliness, to let it flow out of him, and then he found himself writing like a child, of the view. He had looked at his letters to Monica without any relish. What he saw there was a wounded man, whose eyes had become simple. And so he continued to focus on what had not changed, the churches and the cathedrals, and he hated himself for being unable to deal with the changes, even in the buildings.

He remembered how Nora found little details in France delightfully interesting. The tablecloths, the napkins, the counters of the bars, the bread on the tables, the ash-trays, the thin towels, the long pillows; such things only reminded him of travelling to and from the fighting, or forty-eight hours' leave away from it. He could only begin to get absorbed in French history, and especially in ecclesiastical architecture. All his commissions now came from the Catholic Church, and though he was neither a Catholic, nor even religious, he found its fixity helpful. The whole rigmarole of religious celebration helped him to work, to find solutions to pre-ordained questions, rather than to new ones. He thought often of how useful his drawing sessions on the Montagne Sainte Geneviève had turned out to be. Unlike those fragile cadavers, the churches and cathedrals had endured.

Nora remembered his body against hers on the rough sheets of the bed in the French hotel. That thin body which had survived a year in the trenches. That memory which could recite the poems he learnt there. That mind, which was happy to devote itself to endless proportional calculations. And that way of looking, which could see a painter's landscape. She was interested to put all this together, but worried to see how what she loved in her second Herbert was so much to do with a war that she had never known.

A defining experience for a generation but one that she had missed, as a girl, in a family of girls, of Quakers. Was it this knowledge, Lewis's knowledge of a war she had hardly felt, that kept him from her? And the next war, the last one? She had felt desperate at times, alone. Somehow being with Adam only made her feel lonelier. As if things weren't right. She experienced a profound lack of comfort. That was what the woods had given her – reassurance – she thought – and a feeling of rightness. That moment, she still thought of it, so perfect. Their positions together, and the rain outside, was a long moment of harmony for her. Maisky was something else altogether, an intrusion, really, even if she was fascinated by the fact that he found her interesting. That was the opposite of harmony; it continued to be interesting because it was so unequal. He exercised her, whereas the moment in the hut had pacified.

These things had happened. They were over and lived only in her memory. Still to come was Adam; all that energy, curiosity and loneliness. She had loved him too much and never wanted to give him away. Lewis told her she was selfish, and she knew he was probably right. But after what she and Adam had shared, in those village cottages, down those green lanes, away from everyone, she felt she had a right. Lewis hadn't been there.

Lewis tried to bring Nora flowers that were in season: first roses, then Sweet William, and later sweetpeas. As they had no garden now he had to find other ways of getting them; Nora did not like florist's flowers. He asked neighbours, he passed by the allotments, he even stole a few flowers from Regent's Park at night. Adam brought her more sketchbooks, even if they both winced to see her drawings now. He went to university, and his father told him to enjoy himself and not to worry too much. He came back in November and saw his mother very weakened. He came back at Christmas and Lewis told him he had better stay at home, but Adam insisted on going to the hospital.

When Adam returned to Parkhill Road, Lewis knew he had been to the hospital, despite his wishes. They each retired to their own rooms on different floors of the barren house. Nora had hardly lived there. More rented accommodation, with their pieces of increasingly battered furniture making good as far as they could. Nora died just before Christmas. Christmas would never be a good time of year for Adam thereafter, but he never explained.

In the hospital Adam had held his mother's hands, which were shaking a little but still sturdy, and she told him how pleased she was that he was there. She knew Lewis had tried to dissuade him. Neither quite knew why. She told him she wanted him to know he had another name; Geneviève, the patron saint of Paris, because that was where he had been conceived. When he was born on her saint's day, the 3$^{rd}$ of January, she had felt it was a sign of good luck. But he had come into her life so late, she had hardly had enough time to see him into the world.

Nora died prematurely of Parkinson's disease. Other than a few score paintings, she left behind some pieces of Lunéville crockery, the books *Art from the USSR* and *Plats nouveaux!*, three copies of her 'Drawings at the Zoo', published by *The Studio* in 1934, and the pendant inscribed with an elusive French proverb, used by Tolstoy among others. The divorce notice was found online; the letters written from the Front by my grandfather to his sister during the First World War are in my possession. The episodes in the previous pages follow all I know of Nora's life and are as correct as I know how to make them but are essentially fictional.

# Part II

Glasgow was very dark after Lisbon. The pavements were laid in cracked black tarmac, to which dirty lime leaves seemed stuck irrevocably. The terraces were imposingly upright, but sullied. Maria was living on Great Western Terrace, which was, she was regularly told by those she encountered, the jewel of the West End. She had a bed-sitting room, with huge windows made of single panes of glass, their frames tightly painted in as if to prove that they would never need to be opened. There was a little direct light, from late morning until early afternoon, and if there was any sunshine, it fell through the dusty panes to reveal the unattractive floral carpet. She looked across to a long communal garden which had been full of hideous purple rhododendrons in the spring, and behind it, another grand terrace of sandstone houses. Her little kitchen area at the back looked down onto a cobbled lane, with tin dustbins arranged in no apparent order.

Hydrangeas brightened the gloom. In the winter it was almost completely dark before four o'clock, and when she arrived home it already felt like night. In the mornings she had to dress in the dark, and when she walked to work she noticed that the schoolchildren all wore fluorescent armbands for their safety.

They chattered excitedly, apparently oblivious to their terrible privation.

Now and again someone invited Maria for tea, which she learnt was dinner, or for supper, which she learnt was tea. Food was all mixed up. Restaurants were hardly used, except the Indian at the bottom of Byres Road, and that only after an outing to the pub. People were friendly enough, but she had hoped for a little more interaction. Her colleague Delphine was apparently too busy, and Maria found herself talking to the other young scientists who had arrived in Glasgow from England. They, almost more than her, found it hard to believe that they were here, in this famously dangerous city. At its centre an enormous motorway system was being carved out, and Maria could not judge whether the city centre was only temporarily missing, or had never even been there. Everyone seemed a bit lost and getting to Sauchiehall Street near impossible. Somehow the brutal excavations seemed concomitant with the city's reputation, and the possibility of its near complete annihilation.

*

When I hear that the President of the Foundation where I am going to be working comes from the north of Portugal, where Maria de Sousa is based, I guess he most probably knows her. At the end of our first meeting, I ask him if he can help me make contact with her. With a flicker of animation, he looks up from the enormous table between us: 'She is from Porto too! I know her very well.'

That had been my supposition. Here too, people who are or feel themselves to be important like to know other people who are (or feel themselves to be) important.

Also, places matter, especially Porto in distinction to Lisbon. The President takes a well-sharpened pencil from the selection in front of him and, in his tiny meticulous hand, writes 'MARIA DE SOUSA', as a little memorandum. He asks me if I know Portugal and what I have seen so far. Only Lisbon, I said. 'Obidos', he says, writing the name in very tiny capital letters on a bigger sheet of paper, taken from one of the many differently sized blocks on the table. 'Obidos is very attractive.' I take his note with the name OBIDOS at its centre and keep it, more for the charm of the communication than for the information it contains. It takes me five years to go to Obidos, and nearly as long to meet Maria.

*

Maria was pleased to return to Britain from Portugal, even if Glasgow had even less sun than London. She had applied for the job of associate lecturer at the suggestion of Delphine Parrott, a few years her senior, who had moved north to take a job in the Department of Immunology. In London they had worked together at the Institute for Medical Research in Mill Hill where, like Delphine, Maria had become more and more interested in what she persisted in calling the 'leftovers' of mice. Delphine spent much of her working day dissecting mice and her dexterity had already begun to impress her seniors at the Institute. She had already established that, far from being unnecessary, the thymus was crucial to building up immunity when the arrival of this young colleague from Portugal accelerated her study.

Maria was a fish out of water when she arrived at the Institute, and in the beginning, because no one knew what to do with her, she was given a microscope and left alone in what they called the Hut. When she wasn't looking down the microscope Maria could enjoy a nice view of horses in the fields, but in fact she was becoming increasingly involved in the heavy box of glass slides which she had been given to study, and had little need of respite. No one else seemed to be much interested in what they clearly saw as the relics of somebody else's research, but Maria, isolated and uncertain, took pains to make something of it, establishing new sequences across time, looking for patterns in what was still indistinct. And make something of it she did, because she was the first to notice the lacunae in the slides of mice which had been thymectosised, and to understand that here – in the spleen – because the thymus gland was missing, the lymphocytes could not mature. The two women began to work together; as they were both somewhat on the margins of the Institute they had the time and the aptitude to think in new ways. Within two years they had published a joint article in the journal

*Nature,* which identified the lacunae in the lymph cells. This newly defined area – what they called 'eco-taxis' – launched the study of T-cell immunology. Delphine and Maria were on to something, and their colleagues began to take notice, even to feel envy. Maria's PhD was to be on cell traffic and migration, and what was coming to be called 'homing'.

In Glasgow Delphine and Maria encountered another new colleague from Mill Hill. Old professors in Glasgow went by their titles but this new one preferred to be called simply by his first name, Adam. Adam had only recently arrived in Glasgow after leaving Mill Hill, where he had lived on Nan Clark's Lane. Delphine Parrott had learnt the story of Nan from the man at the pub which stood at the corner of Nan Clark's Lane. When Delphine ordered a ham sandwich the publican told her that Mill Hill was full of ghosts. And full of jealous husbands, he added. One of them was the husband of Nan Clark, who had drowned herself in the neighbouring pond. Nan Clark's story stayed with Delphine, and she later relayed it to some of her colleagues, before being regaled with other versions: Nan Clark was drowned by her husband; Nan Clark was drowned by her lover; Nan Clark was drowned by her husband in front of her lover. Whichever was the case, Nan Clark was now known to haunt the lane.

Delphine Parrott loved her work, but she also liked to take a walk at lunchtime and get some fresh air away from the strange chemical amalgams that lingered in the labs. In the 1960s, the fields in Mill

Hill still held sheep, and farmers' wives gave bottles of milk to local children so that they could feed the lambs. They warned the children away from the pond. Delphine found that her lunchtime walks had become increasingly indispensable, but the little pond now invariably provoked an inward shudder as she pictured the terrible scene. She held the image with her for years after, and it was almost as if she, Maria and Adam shared an unspoken secret.

*

In order to improve my Portuguese I read the newspaper *Publico* every day. I spread it out on the table in front of or under the plate from which I eat dinner. I become fond of this moment and of the paper itself, which marks my growing familiarity with the language, and with the country. This is my own chosen homework, additional to my classes, part of my personal routine. I am a newly slow reader, but I have never been more topically informed. I come to know by heart the paper's order, and the order of its priorities and in fact know it better than I have ever known any other paper. I enjoy looking at the newly elected President and the newly elected Prime Minister, smiling individually, smiling at each other. I like their smiles. I stare into them even as the light fades on my terrace and their teeth seem to gleam more brightly. I feel I am in the right place at the right time. Portugal is visibly changing.

*

One surprisingly bright morning as she walked to the lab along Great Western Road Maria saw Adam, the Cell Biology professor, walking ahead of her, briskly. His distinctive white hair shone in the light and his floral tie flapped over his shoulder. He wore a generous gold-coloured corduroy jacket which hung more loosely from his right shoulder than his left, because he was a little lop-sided. He was carrying a leather briefcase and looked as if he had no time to lose. She knew she would not catch him up, but it made her realise that they shared a route to work. Maria was curious to know Adam a little better. She had seen that his department was a new one and full of younger people, mostly men, who had come from London at the same time as she had. And the same time as him. They were different from their Scottish colleagues; they all called each other by their first names, and they never wore suits. Some didn't even wear ties. They were different to the Scots, and even more different to the Portuguese.

*

In November, some two years after I began living in Lisbon, I see, as I eat my dinner, a photo of Maria de Sousa and a photo of the Trustee to whom I report, together on the same page, linked to the same story. Maria de Sousa had won a prize for her promotion of Portugal, which the Trustee was presenting on behalf of the Foundation. So, Maria exists and she is still alive! And my Trustee must know her. The next time I see the Trustee, she is getting into a lift. I rush in after her to say that I'd seen her photo with that of Maria de Sousa. She looks surprised at my unseemly haste. Does she have any contact details, I ask? She says she does. Nothing happens.

*

On occasion Maria and one or two of her colleagues went to the Cell Biology department for a seminar, and sometimes joined the departmental coffee table. There was lots of banter which Maria found difficult to understand at first, but she was happy enough just to listen. She watched the young professor and tried to understand him better. Perhaps she had a hunch that he could help with her research. One evening they met just as they were both leaving the department and so they shared the walk home. This was not very comfortable for Maria, because Adam walked so quickly and seemed not to notice that she didn't. She had a formal coat and bag, whereas he carried nothing, and wore no outdoor clothes. She felt a kind of abandon in this lightness. Trying to keep in step, she rather wished she had not met him now, at least not here, even if she was starting to get his measure in other things. When she tried to talk, she was breathless.

*

Two years later I make a more determined effort. The old President has gone, my trustee has retired, a new President is in place. I meet this President only very occasionally, and always have to wait to be admitted. Despite the comfort of the waiting area – its soft velvet-like carpet, tasteful teak furniture, and not uninteresting collection of modern Portuguese art – these lengthy pauses are hard to digest. For one thing, they seem so old-fashioned. Punctuated by dark-suited personnel stationed at every level, quiet men who sit at small desks with pencil sharpeners, the long corridors and broad stairs lead only to another waiting room. It is perhaps like waiting to be seen by a very expensive private dentist, when it is clear that your own time is much less important than that of the person you are waiting to see. These waits allow the imagination to wander, to other places and times; to discreet and secluded offices and complex chains of command. To film-sets from another era. But this is a film-set without any clear narrative. Restless in a deep leather sofa I recall that Marta, the secretary across the corridor, has also worked for the previous president. Maybe she would have a number for Maria de Sousa? I cross over, anxious that even this might be a transgression, and tentatively set out my case. Marta promises to have a look and to let me know what happens. And sure enough, later that afternoon, she tells me that she has rung. Though she had only got the answering machine, she had left a message.

The following day I am sitting at my computer in the near-subterranean office, looking out on troops of

AFTER NORA

small children dressed identically in candy-coloured hats and smocks. It is a very pretty uniform, but also disquieting; a deceptively irresistible camouflage indicating future homogeneity. The children are lined up in front of their teachers who are coaching them as to the appropriate behaviour for a museum. Most are attentive, but some are diverted by the ducks which are also ranged in lines, with a few stragglers on the margins tempted by the blandishments of visitors to the museum gardens.

Marta rings me directly, a refreshing change in an institution where secretaries ring secretaries prior to connecting directors to directors. She wants me to know that she has spoken with Professor de Sousa. I thank her. There is a pause. It seems that Marta is already aware that this conversation is not an ordinary one. It seems that she wants to be sure that I know this too. Even to warn me.

'Yes, she was very moved... emotional.'

Marta seems anxious to make this point. I am not sure what it would precede.

'She wasn't at home yesterday because she was on dialysis. When she is on dialysis she comes to Lisbon.'

'I see. And what do you think...'

'She wants to invite you to her birthday party. It's on Saturday. Let me give you her number. She said it would give her enormous pleasure if you could go.'

'Thank you so much.'

'She was *quite* emotional', she says again.

I thank her again and make a note of the number, which I put in my bag. I am not going to hurry this.

*

Alongside the mice and the leeches, Adam had begun to work on sponges. More kinds of creatures. Now that he was in Scotland he was diving much more. The more often he dived, the more sea creatures were brought home. Some to eat, some to admire. Some clean, some dirty. Brachiopods, underwater leeches, lobsters, crabs, scallops, even oysters. His daughters had confused their habitats; those underwater with those above ground, as if they alone had access to this other place beneath the sea. Their contributions to the school's nature table seemed to come from a natural world quite different to that of the other children. Their experience of this collision might explain why the story of 'The Little Mermaid' seemed so possible to them. They wondered if they too would have chosen to swap their tails for legs at the cost of losing their voice.

Adam became fascinated by a spot on the West Coast where the water was unusually warm and fertile. He told them that this coastline had previously been joined to Ireland, and that it was just the same over there. Tayvallich was a special place, and one which even his children could share. Adam conducted his experiments on sponges that grew in water so shallow that they too could see what he was doing. And it wasn't as cold as usual. They could tell that their father was excited by this place; its flora and fauna, and its history. He talked to them; telling them more than usual. They were ready to share his excitement, but were confused again when told that they could change into their swimming costumes in Lillie Langtry's bath house. She was the mistress of the Prince of Wales, they learnt, but could not disentangle the idea of being able to walk to Ireland from having your own bath house. When was underwater overwater? When was she here? Was it warmer then? Some such collisions made sense.

*

Parque Eduardo VII runs down to the enormous roundabout named after the Marques de Pombal, with his huge monument at its centre. One dictator portrayed two centuries later by another; a big statue but strangely flaccid. Beyond it lies the Tejo. In most weathers, but not all, the river is as present as if it were the sea.

Walking down the sloping *calçada,* looking out to the water and the hills beyond, provides a sense of almost diversionary relief. (Walking up its slopes, by contrast, towards the Palace of Justice and the Prison, feels quite different.) It is not until the evening of the following day that I feel ready to ring Maria de Sousa. I want to be in the right place, at the right time. I wait till I reach the Parque, knowing that halfway down I can choose one of the dainty wooden benches under the cherry trees and sit there while I make my call. I will look out and down to the river. I will be neither too hot nor too cold. I choose my bench, half in sun and half in shade, and sit down to get out my phone and the piece of paper on which I've noted down Maria's number. I know I am nervous and look down at the Tejo as if for reassurance. I pick out the numbers, Maria answers, and no sooner have I said my name than we both burst into tears.

'Today is my birthday.'

'Today?!'

'Yes, today. You are calling me on my birthday. My eightieth birthday.'

'Your birthday; yes, but I didn't know it was today. But that seems perfect.'

'Your father – how old was he when he died?'

'Eighty-three.'

'Eighty-three', she seems to muse, then she pauses, before changing the subject. 'How long have you been here? Do you speak Portuguese?'

'*Mais ou menos. Quatro anos.*'

'It sounds OK your Portuguese. But I love English. English is my thinking language. Can you come on Saturday?'

'I am not sure, I was meant to be in Porto. I'll have a think.'

'I hope you can. If you can change your plans. We will meet at the Champalimaud Centre at one o'clock. You will recognise me. I'll be in the wheelchair.'

We say goodbye, and I walk further down the hill, choose another bench, half in the sun and half in the shade, and wonder why I am crying.

\*

Adam's growing interest in underwater photography resulted in regular Sunday evening slideshows at home. After he had cooked and they had eaten the seafood he had brought back from his dives he ushered his family from their positions in front of the TV into the unused dining room where he would have erected a rather unstable screen. The girls always made rude remarks about how the slides all looked the same, and how they couldn't tell the leeches apart. Adam could see things they couldn't see, and liked to return to his experience of the depths with more time to consider what was hiding in plain sight. He normally filled the slide tray with one his freshly developed slide films. He dropped the slides in, upside down and back to front. He was practised at this, it was part of his teaching life. The family sat through 24, 48, or 72 slides of sea-bed activity. The images were all ochre-green in colour, with a kind of soft, stringy, squashy aspect that they found repellent. Adam could distinguish one green-brown animal from another but his little audience was not sufficiently interested. Perhaps all that they enjoyed was the novelty of the slide show itself, removed to a different room, doing something together other than eating. The heavy velvet curtains were drawn, the projector whirred, the air became warmer. The evening was punctuated with Latin names. Then came another name. Maria de Sousa. 'Who is that?', they all asked together. 'Maria de Sousa', Adam repeated. There were four more slides of Maria de Sousa lecturing in an ochre-green environment. She was largely hidden by the lectern. He told them that this was the conference which he had gone to in Porto, but he hadn't taken any photos of Porto. No churches, bridges or views. And no other people. Just this ordinary-looking woman giving a lecture. The girls thought little of it, even if this rare overground sighting stayed in their minds in contrast to the underwater life with which they were otherwise surrounded.

*

I was due to take the train to Porto, but I end up rearranging my diary in order to go to the party. I do as I am bid, arriving at the station at Algés and walking back to the Champalimaud Centre. It is a rather bleak bit of Lisbon, with wide fast roads bordered by wasteland, and no pavement to speak of. As I climb onto the raised platform that indicates the boundary with private land, I can see a woman getting out of a large black car and feel almost certain that this is Maria de Sousa, even though she has told me to look out for a wheelchair. Hastening my step, I walk diagonally over the rough tropical lawn towards the car. I feel as if we are in a film. The people gathered around the car look at me as I approach them, I focus on Maria, and we embrace. We hold each other for a while. We step a little apart, each seeing the other with tears.

'I knew it was you, as soon as I saw you.'

'And yet it has been so long.'

'Yes', we both say, feeling the oddness and the rightness of the situation at the same time.

*

Maria's eightieth birthday party was planned as an occasion in which she could thank all the people who had rallied round when she was ill, thank those who had pushed her to get a diagnosis, and those who have continued to support her during the dialysis. About forty people are present, some of whom have come over from the United States. Maria has hired a boat for the occasion, and before long everyone moves onto it. Vinho do Porto is served as we set off from the quay.

When we go to sit down I find that Maria has reserved the place opposite her for me. I protest, saying this isn't merited. Maria insists that Scotland has to have a place at the table. I feel only a little like an imposter, because I can also see that I am wanted, and that this is also evident to the other guests. They have adjusted to me remarkably quickly, and I relish that feeling. I think of how much I am looking forward to getting to know this woman, with whom my father had been in love, and with whom I feel an uncommon affinity. Getting to know her well enough not just to know her myself – as someone who would have more right to be at this birthday celebration – but as a person who had known my father and can explain him to me.

After the main course Maria stands up to make a speech. Her thanks are dedicated to those whose care has meant that she is here today, despite her best efforts (she has been very slow to acknowledge she was ill and needed treatment), and celebrating eighty years. As she speaks Maria looks steadily and constantly across the table at me. Then we eat some puddings, carefully, and the party breaks up, a premature ending occasioned by Maria's next session of dialysis.

The driver tucks Maria into the car and I am asked to join them. We speed away from the other guests and again I feel undeserving. Maria introduces me to the driver, whom she says will take me on to the Santa Apolonia station so that I can take my train to Porto, some hours later than originally planned. Everything has been thought through on my account. Maria is taken to her home, in a modest street near the Champalimaud Centre, and when the driver has got her first into the wheelchair and then into the house, he returns to the car. We drive off to the station.

'We'll be seeing much more of you, I think.'

I feel reassured by my impression that the driver knows everything.

*

We had hardly talked, as yet. But before long Maria phoned inviting me to lunch. It had to be on one of the days when she wasn't at dialysis, nor too depleted, but there were enough of those. I go to Maria's the next Saturday, and am struck by the extreme modesty of the townscape on this coastal strip just west of Lisbon. Arriving too early I explore the environs, trying and

failing to buy a bunch of flowers. Flowers are hard
to come by in Lisbon. I wander in an oblong around
Maria's flat, looking in vain. No such luxuries are
in evidence. I stand in the sun at the dusty edge of a
makeshift car park on the edge of the Algés intersec-
tion waiting for the appointed time to arrive. I wonder
why Maria lives in this roughly constructed bit of town,
bisected by a flyover, and a trainline. At 12:30 sharp I
ring the doorbell with its anonymous designation, 1D,
for first floor right. Names are never used on doors in
Portugal; they say it is because of police surveillance.
That was fifty years ago, but there are still no names.

I have thought in advance about how to manage
this meeting, assuming that I am more determinedly
curious than Maria, but not entirely certain. Though
I want to rush at my questions, I know I must stage
patience. The front door lock clicks and I walk
upstairs to the apartment door, which opens in front
of me. The young Romanian woman who has been
with Maria at the party points to a stool where I can
leave my cardigan and my bag, then gestures towards
the room in front and slips off to the side. Maria is
ensconced in a comfortable chair by the window. The
room is small, and dense, with objects which look as
if they come mainly from the thirties, the fifties and
the seventies. There's a kind of softness of texture:
Maria in cashmere, with a shawl around her shoulders, cushions, wraps and carpet; and a brownness of
tone: clothes, rugs, tables, sideboard, piano, picture
frames. We move to the table and are served a risotto,
pale yellow in colour; its components apparently

carefully calculated to meet Maria's medical needs. Maria raises a toast, saying that she can have just one sip because of her condition. After three studied sips she leaves the wine in its cut crystal glass. We talk a little of the people who had been at the party. We talk of Maria's condition, but only a little. We talk about the piano, which has been in that corner since it was bought for Maria as a child. We talk a little more about her still active life, at the Champalimaud, with friends, in correspondence. New York still seems close, in time, and Porto too, still central. Lisbon is merely a temporary stage, an improvised use of her parents' apartment, which she has never much liked, simply because it is convenient for the dialysis. All this is covered before we arrive at the coffee.

*

In the summers, Maria would return to visit her parents in their small flat in Algés, just west of Belém, itself just west of Lisbon. She found it rather claustrophobic after the spacious houses in Glasgow, and the furniture reminded her of the long stasis of the dictatorship. Maria would enjoy some meals with her parents, play her piano again, using her old sheet music, but before long would look for something to do outside the confines of the small apartment. She could read some of her old books – especially the collections of poetry – but they spoke too much of the past, and no longer reflected her new interests. Even if it was near the Tejo, where her father was a river pilot, their home felt more like a house in the country's interior. There was no view of the river, or indeed, any view at all. Maria had often asked herself whether her father, who had trained for the high seas, but been called back to Lisbon by his wife, was not a little imprisoned. In the small back garden there was a huge lemon tree, which also seemed too large for its cramped environs.

*

We meet fairly regularly. Maria comes to visit my current exhibition with two friends, a designer from America and a colleague from the Champalimaud, whose father's work is to be shown at the museum. Another coincidence. We go around the show together, Maria in a wheelchair, and we lunch in the café. No one says anything of any great import, but the mood is festive. Her friends seem to know already that I am significant to Maria. On another occasion Maria invites me to lunch at the Champalimaud itself, and I first pace and then drift around its great theatrical curves in the mist, alone, until Maria arrives with two other friends, one of them the director of a local Museum. He too has been on the eightieth birthday boat trip. They talk of the Cascais festival, of art and science, of conversations about their connections, of Mario Soares. Maria is described – with an air of knowing amusement which I can't really understand – as his *sábia*. I know only imprecisely what this means; something to do with wisdom, but perhaps more like a 'muse'. So why did they all smile?

And then I feel more strongly that my father was only a very small part of Maria's story, which is properly historical, and would always be foreign to me.

\*

I do not feel that I can ask Maria if she had been in love with my father, or if my father had been love with her. How can I get to the heart of this subject without bringing this new relationship to a premature close? How much time is left?

'Was there a special piece of music which your father loved?', she asks, out of the blue.

'Oh, I'm not sure really', I prevaricate, 'but perhaps Mozart's Horn Concertos? He used to wake us up with those every morning. Why?'

'Because he gave me a record and I left it in a taxi in New York. I always wondered what it was.'

I do not know how to respond.

'He was obviously very knowledgeable about music', averred Maria.

Believing this to be untrue, I hang fire. More than this, I am determined not to talk about what I am sure was my father's ignorance.

\*

'Why did we cry?'

The older woman looks at the younger one as if they both know the answer and there is no need to enunciate it.

'I was very fond of your father.'

'My mother told me that he very nearly left her for you.'

'I am not sure it came to that. I decided to leave Glasgow.'

A sudden reversal of decisions opens up.

'Why?'

'Because I had a good friend in Portugal who had been having a bad time. Her husband was having an affair. When I saw what it did it to her, I didn't want to be responsible for that happening on my account.'

An alternative version which has it that Maria decided to bring things to an end takes me by surprise.

'My mother told me that my father could not forgive you for telling a lie.'

This woman whom I hardly yet know looks strangely arrested. Across the width of the old-fashioned dining-room table, on which is set a plate of biscuits, a small plant, and a bottle of white wine, there is silence, and I fear I have pushed too quickly. The woman takes another small sip from the glass with wine left in it. She seeks and rescues her handkerchief, which is large, animated and unruly, and wipes her nose and her eyes. She adjusts her position and looks back at her questioner.

'I never tell lies.'

This seems to be as far as it is possible to go. And it is quite far, if not far enough. Yes, then, yes; they were in love. This much was clear? No, then, no, not necessarily. But probably, yes, probably.

'Come and look at my books.'

*

In April 1974 Salazar's regime fell and Maria did not
return to Lisbon that summer. She had in any case
already missed out on the euphoria of those spring
days, which had come so quickly and unexpectedly, and was now instead vicariously experiencing
her parents' anxiety about all the uncertainty that
follows a coup. Although she had briefly considered
moving to a Portuguese village to use her medical
training there, she soon realized that she could use
that training to better advantage abroad. The following year she went to see her uncle before he died,
and stayed with her parents. Her mother made her
favourite *Bacalhau à Brás* and they ate together as
they always had. They were a small and loving family
unit, but conversation was slow. Her parents told her
that some cousins were planning to emigrate, afraid
of what might happen at home. They knew this was
not why Maria was living abroad, but as they did not
understand Maria's work in Glasgow they could not
really understand why she lived there. In their different ways they asked an occasional discreet question
about life outside work, but she had little or nothing to
offer in response. She would not even play her piano,
despite or because of her parents' expectations. The
more they encouraged her the more the instrument
seemed to sit in the corner of the living room in silent
recrimination. Their daughter had loved music so
much; why wouldn't she play now? Maria had got
her doctorate – the ostensible reason for her being

in Scotland – but she stayed on, even if her reasons were no longer obvious. She was a lecturer, but they all knew she need not be in Glasgow to lecture. They ascertained, correctly, that neither the climate nor the food was a reason to be there. So, was it the people?

\*

We go next door and spend some time among the piles of books. Maria asks me about my job, the Foundation, the Trustees. She seems to be assessing, in a measured way, whether I have a chance of making a career in Portugal. I want to protest that this isn't about me, but am realising I can't. In different ways it feels as if we both want to go faster than we can in our understanding of the other, but in different directions. I want to know her past, and she, my future. Then we return to the dining room. Maria sits by the window and indicates the lemon tree, too big for its plot, too luxurious for its surroundings, too rural for the city. It seems to represent the other, better side of a life now constrained.

'My father planted the lemon tree. It has always been very healthy. They grow well here. We'll give you some lemons to take home. Another time we can give you tangerines. My mother liked them more; she made tangerine sorbet.'

I go home with a plastic bag full of lemons; large and lumpy. They bump against my legs as I walk over the uneven ground of the unfinished terrains around the station, going through the underpass towards the platform for the train that will take me back to the centre. I have a sense of having already very nearly arrived at my destination.

*

When Maria was home she usually made a visit to her childhood friend Teresa, in Coimbra, whom she now sensed had become slightly troubled. She took an early train from Santa Apolonia to Coimbra and met Teresa for lunch in a restaurant they often went to. Teresa thought this was the kind of restaurant Maria had been missing. Maria had always taken food seriously, and she liked restaurants that showed some ambition without being pretentious. They met outside at the bottom of the steps, looking down the street with its pretty trees and ancient church. Teresa looked different, Maria could see at once. They embraced each other and took a table. As always they eschewed the small plates laid out to entice the unwary and focused on the menu of the day. The blackboard showed nothing new; indeed Maria could have recited the menu by heart, but if she could at times be flippant about Portuguese cooking, now she was in the mood for its comforting familiarity. They both ordered the duck rice, a classic dish. It only ever varied so slightly that it elicited no comment and they ate it as if they were at home. It was late August, and without the students around, the town was even quieter than usual. Of the other tables outside, only a few were occupied. Theirs was under a tree, between sun and shade, dappled by the breeze. The food arrived promptly. They unfurled their napkins, stretched out their legs, settling in for a good talk.

'So, how are the castles in Scotland?' teased Teresa.

'I haven't seen any yet', said Maria, 'but I will, I am sure, before long. But more importantly, how are you? Or you and Fernando?'

'Well', said Teresa hesitantly, taking a sip of water.

She had already thought about this conversation with Maria many times, wanting her to be back so that she could get it started. But now, it was hard to know how to do that.

'It's not like it was', she began 'He is much less interested in me, in doing things with me, even in how I am. Maybe that is just how it is. Or, maybe, there is another reason, but I don't know. It makes me feel lonely, but I'm trying to adjust. Maybe my expectations were anyway too high.'

'Maybe', said Maria. 'You two were very, very close and maybe that can't last. But do you think his attention is elsewhere?'

Teresa told her she was trying not to think about it, not to let her curiosity get the better of her, not even to imagine. For now, she would rather keep things calm. Maybe they could talk instead about Maria, and her much more exciting life abroad?

'Mmmn', said Maria, oddly equivocal. 'You know that already, mostly. The dark, the wet, the chill. But the science is good, and the teams, and I like the atmosphere in the lab. All the people are really very young, even the professors. And it is quite sociable;

you even get invited to people's houses, which is nice. I think it is partly because most of us are from other places. Mostly England though. Not so much abroad. And everyone pronounces my name wrong. They all call me Maria de *Suuuuza*.'

Maria drew out the vowel and pulled a face. They smiled.

'Tell me more. Tell me about who you work with, who you like.'

'Well you know how much I like Delphine, but she is pretty busy, so I see much less of her nowadays.' Maria sat back, recrossed her legs, lifted her right hand up to her left cheek, and held her silence.

'So...' said Teresa.

'So', echoed Maria.

She looked around her, up at the plane trees, through them to the sky and the wispy clouds, out to the heavy Salazarist buildings, down to the cobbles. She put her hands in her lap, resting on the thick cotton folds of her new summer dress. Catching the eye of the waiter, she signalled that she wanted to pay the bill. He came swiftly over and she paid just as promptly. The bill seemed ridiculously small now that she was paid in sterling.

They got up together, suddenly aware that the meal, habitually slow, had come to a sudden end. Each wondered whether the other had noticed her reticence, or rather, to what extent. They exchanged glances and embraced. Pulling back, they held each other by the elbows and smiled again, more openly, more winningly. 'Let's walk and talk', suggested

Teresa, manoeuvring Maria out of the restaurant and up the street. They headed towards the botanical garden, a place they both loved, and a place where they had often talked before. Descending the palatial steps, Teresa turned back to Maria, who was smaller and heavier than she and always lagged a little behind.

'I know you have a new private life, I can tell. And I suppose it's quite different there. It's all new, and different, isn't it, after Portugal. You're liberated!'

Teresa ended this in an attempted American accent, raising her eyebrows as she accentuated the last word. 'Liberated.'

\*

Maria and I continue to see each other. Naturally enough the woman I had seen in my father's slides wants to talk about the present, even if I want to talk about the past. This feels like a gentle battle of wills, one which I think Maria will win. She seems to be in no hurry, and I envy her controlled pace. But when I mention how often, and how routinely, taxi drivers ask me if I appreciate Portugal, by which they mean its climate and cuisine, I touch a nerve.

'Hrruphah!' she exclaims. 'That is the trouble with Portugal. Still. As if the climate and the cuisine is all that matters. It is pathetic. Quite pathetic. A sign of low expectations, the complete absence of ambition.'

I venture that I think it is different with the new generation, though I am sympathetic to Maria's outburst. And indeed she opens my eyes to something I have never thought much about, other than to recount the phenomenon with amusement. Maria does not ask me the other more usual questions: are you married and do you have children? Perhaps she knows better. But then, neither do the taxi drivers. I begin to understand how her exasperation with Portugal – with the remnants of a complacency resulting from its long dictatorship – will still occasionally bubble up and how it betokens that same and stronger exasperation which took her abroad. She never asks me why I have left Britain, but she must empathise with my situation to the extent that she does not feel the need to ask.

*

Maria knew Adam was speaking at the conference in Porto. Adam knew Maria was speaking at the conference in Porto. They did not speak to each other about it. Maria went to stay with an old friend from university. Adam stayed in the Hotel Infante Sagres. On the first free afternoon, instead of joining the coach for the sightseeing trip, Maria suggested to Adam that she show him round. She took him to what she called the inside-out churches with blue and white tiles covering their outer walls, and the market, and then they went down to take a better look at Eiffel's bridge. At this point Maria realised it would be nice to take a boat trip up the Douro, so they went along to a jetty to buy a ticket and waited for the next embarkation.

Neither was very good at waiting, but Maria was better than Adam, who was visibly impatient. 'Ice-cream?' she suggested, as a way of helping them through and he nodded emphatically. They crossed the road and Maria bought the ice-creams.

The next morning Maria lay in bed and imagined Adam opening the shutters of his room and looked down the dark granite street with its fancy baroque belltowers. She knew he got up early. She pictured him deciding to take a walk before breakfast; getting shaved, dressed, choosing one of his many floral ties to go with one of his coloured shirts. She doubted that he could quite get the measure of Porto. It was at once austere and almost Scottish, but also southern. He would see that camellias flourished, and plants in general. It would probably remind him of Edinburgh, with its sudden ups and downs, and sooty appearance. And he would see the poverty, unless it was too like Scotland to be noticeable.

*

In the new year I engineer the chance to see an architecture exhibition in Dafundo and to follow it with lunch at Maria's. It is a little out of my line of work, but it is a way of fitting in with Maria's medical schedule. I get off the train at Cruz Quebrada, a desolate suburban station, covered in graffiti, with a trace of the beach combined with a trace of its name, 'broken cross'. Even finding the way out of the station is not obvious, and locating the Order of Architects is harder. The architect whose work is on show was born in 1929 (fully ten years before Maria) and is still practising. He is there himself at the exhibition, as are his family. He stands upright beside his models; meanwhile, in stark contrast with his punctilious courtesy, his daughter and her sons are curled up on a bench looking at their phones.

Continuing the journey from Dafundo along the coast to Rua Dom Jeronimo Osorio is surprisingly unpleasant. I have the sensation of walking under a cliff, but with old factories or deserted industrial frontages making up its face. It is bleak and dusty, unrelieved in any way. The cars whizz past unthinkingly. The pavement is narrow and I feel vulnerable. I ask myself again why on earth Maria lives here when she speaks with such nostalgia of her house in Porto. Surely she could have suitable medical attention there? It seems too dreary for one who so fully appreciates life.

*

The first session of the conference in Porto began with Maria's paper. Adam sat halfway back on the right-hand side. The university auditorium was slightly raked, and he had a good view of the stage. Some time after Maria had taken the floor he felt impelled to take a photo, with his large camera, which he had to take out of its case before adjusting the readings in the semi-light. He was quite used to handling the equipment in the dark after all the time he spent underwater, where he took most of his photographs. In fact there was something almost sub-aquatic about this environment. He took a picture of Maria at the lectern as she explained a slide, looking towards the screen, lively with her own curiosity. In her concern to communicate its imagery she momen-tarily forgot her audience. Then he took another. And two more. His neighbours looked at him quizzically. No-one else took a photograph in a lecture. Of a lec-turer. And obviously it wouldn't be a very good slide. Adam too knew it would be grainy if not blurred. He knew it would also be hard to look at and he regretted that, already.

In the evening there was a concert for all the del-egates. It was held in the Coliseu and although it was only a short walk they were taken there by bus. Adam and Maria sat at the front, she neatly tucked in by the window, his long legs trailing in the corridor. Adam never went to concerts, but there was no good reason not to follow the crowd on this occasion. Maria told him that she loved to hear the piano, and had even, for a time, thought she might try to become a professional pianist. In fact the only reason why she had stopped playing in Glasgow was because she didn't have a piano. That evening, she told him, would be a treat. Maria João Pires was to play Beethoven. She had recently won a big prize in Brussels for her interpretation. She too was living abroad. Perhaps Maria empathised with what she saw as the pianist's response to the situation at home, and keenly identified with a woman who had left Portugal to follow her vocation.

Adam fell asleep as soon as the lights went down. He woke when Maria pressed his arm and he attuned himself to his new environment. At the interval Maria went off to get drinks and was away longer than either anticipated; she hadn't been home for a while and was detained in the foyer by friends and acquaintances; such was her gregarious nature. Adam remained in the hall, a little fazed by his position. He could not talk about the music, he did not know the piece, or the pianist, and he felt himself a little uncomfortable, trailing in Maria's wake. There was a piano in his house, which nobody even used, and he realised that, in several ways, there was no point mentioning it. He knew similarly that there was little point mentioning that Janet Baker had stayed with their neighbours, despite learning how much her Dido had meant to Maria. Learning, but not learning enough. What had Dido meant to Maria exactly? He didn't know how to ask the question. Yet he knew that she was not at all discomfited by his inability to respond, and indeed, enjoyed the fact that they both knew that she was altogether in her element. Her eyes, which were always bright, now positively sparkled. She was not just enjoying the evening, she was also revelling in explaining her enjoyment.

'This is a very special evening; I am glad they got it right,' she said.

'The right music, the right musician?' he queried.

'The right music, the right musician, yes, indeed. And the right companion,' she added a little tentatively, but with mischief too.

'A night-time rendezvous and not a mouse in sight.'

'Oh, I'm sure they're here. Listening! Can't you hear them? Eek, eek.'

'Do they speak English?'

'They speak every language, don't you know. They know no limits.'

'And nor do we', he said, and regretted it immediately.

*

Now I know her street, dull in appearance, and I know there are no florists here. I know the door in the small block. I know the floor, and where to turn in, and where to sit down. I know we will eat a small lunch promptly, and that it will be served by Aurora. This time however Aurora ventures to tell me, when I help get some water, that she is working too hard. That she has little time off. That she has not been home for a long time. Certainly her little bed, tucked in behind the kitchen, speaks of another age. Maria is just as vocal in extolling Aurora's ability to cook to her needs, and to monitor her intake, but now I notice the strictness evident in her voice. As we sit at the little dining table I feel myself to be in an odd position, Maria is a new acquaintance with a long back-story that I hardly know even though I play a part in it. And she in mine.

*

Maria walked Adam back to the Hotel Infanta Sagres. She came inside for a nightcap and their discussion quickly turned to the conference. Maria was principally pleased that it should happen in Portugal, at all. For her this was a sign of better times ahead in her home country. Adam made damning remarks about that morning's speakers, and they laughed. Neither indulged in small talk, whether from choice or inability, but each had a vein of absurdist fantasy which amused the other. Maria was much readier to praise, whereas Adam preferred to lampoon. She tempered his remarks with well-chosen qualifications; he accepted them readily enough, silently absorbing the fact that for him this was a new experience.

Maria told Adam she had remembered a painting in which Maria João Pires was sitting with two other women. It had stayed in her mind, with its strong simple outlines, like silhouettes, and a clear sense of waiting. None of them was doing anything. They were all artists, of different kinds, but their hands were at rest. Idle. It was like a picture of total inertia, set in a barren space, devoid of attributes. In truth Pires had escaped this inertia by leaving Portugal. As had she.

But the painter was prescient; it was a painting made at the very threshold of change. Just before the revolution. She couldn't remember who the others were, writers she thought. A poet? Yes, it must have been Natália Correia. She was sitting up, maybe more like a figure on a Greek vase? Maria's image was imprecise, but she remembered a sense of space that was similar to that on the vases; flat, shallow, and yet unlimited. Three women waiting. But not forever.

Maria put all this to Adam, a little disjointedly, but it was enough for him to absorb and to think again: she knows more, or she knows differently. She has a political consciousness that goes deeper than mine does; she knows about Portugal, of course, and music, okay, painting, too, but all these things join up with her. She sees the links, she makes them make sense. This is a worldview such as he had never encountered. For perhaps the first time in his life, Adam was taken outside of himself. He no longer had his wife to rely on for conventional conversation, and he realised that he rather liked that. His stepmother had told so many people that he was lucky to have a wife who knew how to converse that he had almost forgotten that he too could talk. And listen, when he wished. And he didn't mind silences either.

*

The painting of the three women is by a painter called Nikias Skapinakis. Natália Correia sits on a bent-wood cafe chair, and the woman who sits at her feet beside Maria João Pires is the writer Fernanda Botelho. Their dresses are painted in flat tints of green, black and blue, like patterns for clothes, cut for assembly. The women on the floor look at the viewer, whereas the older Correia is shown in profile, her gaze lost to the distance. I choose this painting as the work with which to talk about the lockdown, or confinement, as it is called in Portuguese, which always seems an oddly femininised way in which to describe being kept indoors. The more I think about this painting, the more I like it. It allows me to link my growing understanding of the country (it is part of a series described as a study of melancholy in Portugal) with my experience of the pandemic. I even make a short film in which I sit at a piano which I cannot play, talking about women who seem immobilized.

*

On his return to Glasgow Adam decided to build himself a stereo record player. His wife asked why on earth he suddenly wanted to listen to records. His daughters asked why he couldn't just buy a ready-made record player. But Adam seemed determined to build it himself, and bought lots of electrical parts from various audio specialists. It worked, but was a jumble of wires and bits and pieces. He decided to clad it in mahogany. For this he went down to the junk shops on the Dumbarton Road and bought an enormous old chest of drawers, which he then proceeded to cut up. After many evenings of sawing, glueing and clamping, the new stereo system was set up in the drawing room, carefully arranged so that the places where you could see the sawn edges and the beads of glue which held the whole together were not quite so obvious. Adam went out to buy some records with which to test it, and came back with Mozart's Piano Concertos 20 and 27. Played by Maria

João Pires. Then he bought Mozart's Horn Concertos 1–4 and put them on every morning before he made breakfast. They replaced his morning wake-up call, and his daughters liked their happy tone. His wife just said it was too loud. In later years the girls would look back and associate this fanfare with the break of day, and with their father. Otherwise they did not share this new interest, which involved their father going upstairs after dinner and sitting there alone listening to music. Behind a closed door.

\*

From Porto, Maria had gone down to visit Teresa in Coimbra. Teresa hadn't asked her to come, but Maria thought the timing was good, and the geography better. The last letter she had received from Teresa was short, and not at all like her. She had written a card, saying simply, 'Dear Maria, I am glad to think your work is going well and that Glasgow is good for you. This thought is good for me, kisses.'

They had arranged to meet by the Museum. It had beautiful carvings in the local stone, badly eroded, but perhaps the more beautiful for that. There were several cafés nearby and they chose one, silently, without reference to each other. Their mood was sombre. Maria held Teresa's hand on the table and, looking directly at her, made Teresa return her gaze. Within a second or two Teresa had looked away, and down, and got out a handkerchief. Then she cried. Maria gave her another handkerchief. The waiter was deferential, quickly establishing that Maria had been away and had a lot to catch up on, especially in this year of revolution. But Maria had talked enough with her parents, whom she phoned punctiliously, to know what 1974 had brought. What she needed to be here to understand was Teresa's situation. Teresa did not know if Fernando was sleeping with this girl – Isabel – but that wasn't what hurt. It was rather that he preferred her company. Teresa had never seen them properly together, but she could imagine, all too well, how he would hang on Isabel's words, make jokes just for her, share confidences. Teresa had become the one who didn't listen, who didn't share, who didn't laugh with him. He told her that Isabel was just more interested (and he surely meant just more interested in him). Fernando continued to live with Teresa and the children, eating breakfast, lunch and dinner with them, but he spent any free time he had (or could make) with Isabel. He wanted to leave Teresa, but didn't know how. Teresa, who was normally of an optimistic, practical frame of mind, had become wrung out by her unhappy situation, equally unsure whether she wanted him to go or stay. Maria really did not know how to say anything that would sound wise, encouraging, or helpful. As she thought about how to be properly sympathetic, she glimpsed another way in which to understand the story, to be the Isabel and not the Teresa, and turned away from this thought. Instead she focused on the fact that she had a job that meant as much to her as a marriage. She hoped it would last as long, or longer, and be more reliable.

Teresa and Maria split the bill. They put on their gloves and snapped their handbags shut. They got up and walked cautiously out onto the *calçada*, knowing that their smooth leather soles might slip on the treacherous limestone pavement. Men were returning to work after lunch, almost identical in their suits and ties and hats, all with umbrellas in hand. They moved off in groups; fours, three, twos. Only very occasionally alone. Jokes sailed on after them, flying through the air like parting shots. They were a brotherhood, these daily diners, strong against all comers. Strong against all women. The plane trees rustled their remaining leaves; those which had already fallen tumbled over the pavement, making a rasping noise as they caught on the edges of the black and white stones before being moved along by the breeze.

*

Maria and Teresa wrote to each other quite regularly. Maria was always pleased to see an envelope with a Portuguese stamp, especially one with Teresa's large sloping hand.

'Querida Maria, now I know and I wish I didn't. Fernando has become somehow fascinated by our neighbour's daughter, who often visits her. She is pretty, but I don't think that it is especially about prettiness. No, what is worse, I think, is that he seems to think her kinder than me. This is what he says, at least he keeps saying how kind she is, how sympathetic. He has helped her bring things into the house, and even taken things from her mother's to her house. He helps her do things that he would never do for me. Never even think of doing. And I wouldn't think of asking. That makes me cross, and sad, but if I say that of course it sounds jealous, and ridiculous. So I have tried very hard not to. But yesterday, when I wanted Fernando to collect the children from school, he said he couldn't as he had promised to take some pumpkins round to her house. A small thing, but it made me so cross with him. And then, as I waited at the school for A and R, cross with myself. So, there you have it, an age-old tale. Trust you are keeping well, not too cold, not too wet, and that work is going well. A hug, kisses. T.'

Maria was surprised by this letter. Partly because Teresa had never had anything problematic to write about before. All their usual confidences – which were hardly even confidential – were positive; what they were reading, trips, parents, mutual acquaintances, a good recipe, a new song, a special flower. And partly because Teresa had never used letters in this way; they would have talked. Now, for the first time, a problem which Teresa had gone to the trouble of setting out on paper. This opened up a new space between them, spanning the difference between the experience and the recounting. Maria felt more aware of the gap between home and away, her different personas. She felt more responsible.

*

Maria calls Aurora and asks for a blanket. She says she is feeling chilly, and she links it to a concern she has about the cleanliness regime in the clinic. She isn't impressed, and has already complained. Now that there is this new virus she is more anxious than before. And she is tired.

Maria moves over to a lower daybed opposite her chair and Aurora covers her with a blanket. Aurora leaves the room and Maria extends her hand.

'Your father and I liked to laugh. He had such a sense of humour. One does not often find that combination: a great scientific curiosity and a good sense of humour. We laughed together. At the same things. Now I must rest.'

'Aurora!' she calls, 'She has to go now.'

*

In Glasgow Maria's work was going well. And she felt more at home. In part, she knew, this was because Adam had been kind to her in his lab, and had made a point of inviting her in to see his mice, the little ones he fed every night. He had some unusual varieties and they amused each other watching the mice turn circles, or bed down in matchboxes.

Sometimes, at the weekends, when he had to come in to feed the mice, or the leeches, Adam found her there. Maria had dared to ask him to measure the adhesiveness of her lymphocytes, which he agreed to do, and did, even when she sent him too many boxes. The lab was cosy compared to her flat, and there was a comfort in the machines gently gurgling, or warming, or rotating. Lights flashed or glowed in the darkened room. She liked the feeling that everything was quietly staying alive. They shared notes on their research. Their discussions about the environments or habitats of cells resonated with Maria, who was busy adapting herself to her new habitat, or vice versa.

On one occasion, when Adam was about to overtake Maria at the Byres Road crossing, he suggested that they take a little walk in the Botanics. She had previously taken a cursory look but had not been impressed. After Coimbra, or even Lisbon, they seemed dully municipal. No drama, no scholarship, no exotic trees. Adam agreed with what she said. The Gardens were hardly worthy of the name Botanical, but the Kibble Palace was still a beautiful structure, and besides, if they walked around the lawns, he might find her a four-leaf clover. This seemed a rather romantic gesture and it made Maria's heart thump a little. She watched his long figure stride up the green slope and she followed at a distance. Then she sat on a bench beside a crescent of begonias and waited. She crossed her legs at the ankles and crossed her forearms around her handbag, sitting very upright and watching families making the most of the late evening light. Before very long he came back triumphantly with two between his fingers. 'One for you and one for me. Keep it safe for luck'. She did.

*

'I promised myself not to ask any more questions of this nature, but I have to ask you, sorry, but where does the four-leaf clover come from?'

We both looked at a large wooden frame and, inside, at the centre of the mount, a single four-leaf clover.

'Why do you ask?'

'Because Adam had a gift for finding four-leaf clovers. He had a collection.'

'Maybe it came from him then. Yes, maybe it did.'

*

After she had finished her Ph.D. Maria had more time for free research. This allowed her to do more work with Adam, and together they published two articles on cell adhesion in lymphoid cells. They worked on the mice together, and the mice were a reason to go into the lab at weekends or to return there in the evening. They had to be fed. Adam was as faithful to their mealtimes as his family to theirs. In the evening the lab was quiet, the lights lowered, and only the machines seemed alive, apart from the mice and their two guardians. Adam and Maria made a point of not arranging to meet outside office hours, but delighting in coincidence. The work was slow but promising, and when they published their joint research on 'Lymphocyte interactions and positioning' they confidently numbered it 'Part I'.

They complemented each other well: Adam was more impetuous, Maria more strategic. They did not need to express their delight in finding a work partner who was curious, restless and unconventional. More unexpected was the warmth they found expressing for each other, if only obliquely, with unexpected gifts or unlikely remarks that made them laugh out loud. Each was more than a bit of a show-off, both were only children used to being noticed. But rarely, if ever, had either met anyone who sparked back; equally quick, funny, and off-the-wall. They saved up amusing aperçus for each other, knowing the belly laugh (Adam) or chortle (Maria) that would follow suit. The only person who noticed the nature of this meeting of minds was Delphine Parrott, who generally kept her distance. So when Delphine asked Maria if they could talk, Maria knew it was significant. They met in the University Café on the Byres Road and sat facing each other in a booth. They looked surprisingly similar. Delphine might have been Maria's sister. In their different ways they were both old-fashioned; Delphine was anyway ten years older, while Maria had grown up in a country that was very cut off from larger developments. They both dressed formally, more 1950s than 1975.

In Britain Maria had learnt to order tea rather than coffee. Tea for two. Delphine was poised. She allowed Maria to pour out the tea and then she elegantly added the milk. She pushed Maria's cup and saucer towards her and placed her hands around her own. Looking down into the cup, Delphine quickly reviewed her objectives, and her motivations. She had already suffered moments of bad professional remorse and disappointment, noticing how her own research had been insufficiently acknowledged, and knowing how few colleagues had supported her promotion to professor, the first female professor in the university. She wanted to advise Maria, who had a better chance than she to avoid these pitfalls, but she also felt an unprofessional bitterness, seeing how Maria radiated a happiness that was more than just professional. And knowing that she still had the chance to enjoy it.

'Maria, your work with Adam is inspiring, and mostly without fault. Even if I had one or two queries, I don't want to go into them now.'

You think I've made a *faux pas*?'

'Not yet, no, but you may very soon.'

'How?'

'There's no point being defensive. I know you well enough. I just want you to think through your situation, that's all. No-one else will tell you this, but I feel I should. And I've known you much longer than anyone else in Glasgow.'

At first Maria had been sure that Delphine wanted to talk about the research papers. Maybe they had been too quick to publish, or hadn't acknowledged Delphine properly? But then she saw that Delphine wasn't talking about science.

'What have I done wrong?'

'Maria, Maria, nothing yet, specifically. As far as I know. But it will happen. That's obvious.'

'What are you referring to, will you be clear?'

'Please don't pretend you don't know'.

'OK, you don't like me working with Adam.'

'I don't mind you working with Adam. That is irrelevant, really. Obviously you get on and produce good work together. But you're falling in love with him. And he with you. Then what?'

Then we can be in love, Maria wanted to say, but she didn't. Instead she said nothing at all, hearing the obvious truth spoken, breaking the spell she had been enjoying for months. She looked at Delphine, this elegant, older colleague, professionally successful. She thought of all the work Delphine had done on pregnancy, abortion and reproduction. But always living alone. A quick, unfocused thought ran across her brain, relating to Delphine's solitude. She thought of the work they had both done on habitats, on the natural journey which cells will take to find the place where they will flourish. She thought, they were both alone really, even if she still might reproduce. Theoretically at least. With who?

Then she thought about Teresa. They had been at school together. Teresa was by no means as clever as Maria and married Fernando shortly after they left. Fernando was a pharmacist, four years older, and full of drive. Although Teresa did an accountancy course, as soon as she was pregnant she settled down to make a home. By the time her children were reaching secondary school Maria was in Glasgow doing her PhD Fernando was involved in the pharmaceutical industry, and curious, often indignant, about the way it was evolving. Teresa had nothing to say about that, or about the new form of post-revolutionary life over which people were endlessly quarrelling. Her needs seemed too simple, and Fernando wanted her to want more. She cared about making him happy, and the more she cared, the less he was. Fernando found himself almost wishing that Teresa had taken up the cause of women's liberation. At that point Teresa had asked Maria about women's lives in Britain, but Maria knew that that was not at the root of her question. She understood Fernando's frustration, because the limits of Teresa's outlook were just as clear to her. But she also knew that all that she loved in Teresa was contained in that simple trust, which he now rejected. Delphine looked at Maria expectantly over her teacup. Maria looked back with a curious mixture of expressions: defiance, regret, understanding. Maria had never asked Delphine about her emotional life. She was surprised and slightly outraged that Delphine should have taken this upon herself. But she also acknowledged it was wise, and well meant.

'Yes, you are right. I must make something happen.'

'Happen?', said Delphine, with some alarm.

'Not to him. With me.'

'What does that mean?'

Maria thought about that large house where Adam lived with his wife and daughters. She had been there on rare occasions, and only with other people. It was full of things. Big pieces of furniture, lots of paintings, books, plants, pets. A piano. She thought of herself inside it, imploding or exploding. She doubted Adam would take any step.

'I will have to move on'.

Delphine's reaction was unexpected. She feared that perhaps her own motives had been misplaced, that she had been jealous, and that she was cheating Maria out of something that she, Delphine, would come to regret.

'Move on?', she said weakly.

'Yes', said Maria, more firmly. 'I have to get out of the picture.'

Maria carried with her the image of Teresa, and now she had really to admit to herself that she was 'the other woman' in the story.

\*

Maria phones me to say she is rested and feels better. I tell her that I am quarantining in my apartment. The Foundation has asked me to come back from my brief trip abroad so as to be ready to resume work, but they want me to quarantine first. I can only acquiesce. I imagine that one or two friends who live locally will be ready at least to take a walk with me, even at a distance, but I am wrong. I decide to make the best of it and instead to work hard at finishing off my novel about Nora. I take my daily walk up the hill to Parque Eduardo Septimo, or down the hill to the Tejo. I see no-one I know, and most of the people who are out and about are accompanied by a dog. There are small groups of police spread out across the parks. All the benches are taped off to stop people sitting and lingering. The only person who rings me every day is Maria de Sousa.

'Are you OK?'

'Yes, thank you.'

'What are you doing?'

'I am just finishing off my novel.'

'Oh my word, a novel?'

'Yes. I was already writing it before, but now I have pretty much finished it.'

'What is it about?'

'Well, it's about my grandmother. But as I never knew her, it is mostly fictional.'

'And why her?'

'Oh, well, I suppose it began with my father's funeral, and getting my facts right for my speech, and then discovering things that were not the same as we'd been told, or even quite different. I just checked a few things and then unexpectedly found things, simply by searching online. Like her divorce. And to see that in print was somehow shocking.'

'Good writing. Goodbye for now.'

And so she rings off, quickly, as if she has lots more people to ring, and she probably does.

\*

Adam was invited to teach a course on Invertebrate Immunology at the University of the West Indies. The campus would be the Discovery Bay Marine Laboratory. A trip to Jamaica excited his daughters, who were suddenly keen once again to be part of the family unit, even though they had virtually left home, and whether or not their father was taken up with diving and teaching. On campus parents were strangely removed from their children, who slept in the students' dormitory as if fully independent. There they eyed up the other girls' sleepwear, surprised by the way it looked just like daywear. Their own nightdresses suddenly seemed Victorian. The American students looked as if they were ready for action. Parents slept across the campus, in the apartments reserved for staff and visiting professors. But midway through the taught course everything was interrupted by the imminence of Hurricane Allen. The Americans mostly knew what to do, but for the British the preparations were entirely novel. They were coached in the appropriate etiquette and spent hours taping windows and endlessly sweeping the concrete yards to clear them of any loose matter. As the storm approached everyone at the lab packed an overnight bag and retired into the hills to spend the night in wealthy people's houses, hoping for the best. There was a strange atmosphere among them, half midnight feast, half nuclear shelter. Some of the group stayed up into the night, drinking rum and coke. Others bedded down with cushions and blankets, lying along the edges of the room behind the settees. In the morning, when they woke up, each in their own improvised space, everything looked exactly as it had the night before. A sense of anti-climax preceded their relief. They promptly drove down to the coast and even there the lab looked unscathed. The girls' scepticism was countered, however, by their growing realisation that all the scientists were now focused on the sea. The storm had hit off the coast, and the reef would be damaged. Leaving the hangers-on to enjoy a makeshift breakfast, the divers all got ready to go in. And so it emerged, with trip after trip, that the reef had taken the brunt of the damage, which meant an enormous loss of habitat, and a corresponding loss of experimental work, recorded over decades. Now after Hurricane Allen the split between staff and students manifested itself differently. Those left on land felt more keenly their secondary status while those who dived turned their attentions to the destructive effects which the hurricane had wrought upon the coral reef. Routines only recently established were now overturned. The loss of electricity entailed a variety of changes, and the library was no longer an air-conditioned haven. While Adam gathered marine data, Ann smoked and drank more than usual, and ran out of light reading. She had nothing she needed to do, and nothing much she wanted to do. She didn't like the heat and she didn't like the water. When the girls got tired of their own activities, they might pay their mother a visit. This did not happen very often, as mostly they were happy enough to be in the communal areas. Her flat was on the upper level, and to reach it they passed trays of basil, from seeds planted by their father as soon as he arrived, and already abundant. Hibiscus and bougainvillea entwined the simple metal balcony. At the far end of the room, as if at the farthest remove, their mother seemed to hide in the corner. They had not given much thought to her, so keen were they on developing their suntans and fitting in to the new context. They, like their father, relished the sun; only their mother stayed out of its way. During this time her relation to her daughters shifted, and they began to see her more objectively, detached from the family unit, alone.

Settling down with her mother, in a way she rarely did, both of them stilled by the oppressive heat, her elder daughter found her newly accessible to serious conversation. Her mother tentatively suggested that this was the moment at which her daughters would need to choose a route. Would they follow Adam or Ann; take a supportive role like her, or have a career, like him? They talked about those choices, which had never seemed problematic for Ann, at least not at the outset or for quite a long while. It was only when Adam had shown his preference for women with careers that she had had any doubts at all. And still she was pleased to have been a wife and mother.

'But wait a minute, what do you mean by Adam's preferences? Who are you talking about?'

'Well you know how Adam has had admirers. Mia, for example, she would have loved to go off with him.'

'But how serious was that?'

'Not very, I think, at least for him. But she certainly flattered his vanity.'

'And who else?'

'Well, the most serious one was Maria de Sousa.'

'And was that reciprocated?'

'Yes, yes, quite a lot.'

'So it was serious?'

'Adam was certainly serious. He was certainly thinking about leaving me for her.'

Maria de Sousa! The woman in the slides. The small woman in the dark brown room. Adam leaving her mother. (Adam leaving them all.)

'But she wasn't especially attractive, was she?'

'No, but she was interesting. That is what he always said. He said she had an original mind.'

The pair of them sat together, closer than usual, on two opposing day beds, nestling in the corner of the room. The temperature was high; the Venetian blinds were let down and threw their shadows across the furniture and down onto the bare floor. There was almost no noise as they sat there absorbing this unique conversation and the circumstances which had provoked it. Suddenly they heard the cries of a goat. They knew it was being slaughtered for their dinner. Every day another little goat was brought down from the interior of the island in a pick-up truck, standing alone on the galvanised metal, like a singular trophy, shackled at its ankles. This would go on until the Discovery Bay Laboratory had built up sufficient supplies of meat to replace what had been lost when the freezers went off. They paused to digest this image. Then everything fell silent again.

'And what happened?'

'He was thinking very seriously about leaving, but something happened that put him off. He said she had lied. It was something to do with a parcel, or the post. That she had sent something when she hadn't. He couldn't forgive her. That was the end.'

This explanation seemed inadequate. It was perhaps a part of the truth, but surely only a part. And it explained Adam's behaviour as if Maria had had no part in it. Maria de Sousa's name never came up again after that.

*

'How are you tonight?'

'OK thank you; and you?'

'Still worried about my clinic, which is not doing things right. But it's worse in Britain. Promise me you won't go back there. They are doing everything wrong there.'

(I demur, having no clear plan in any case.)

'No, in general, Portugal is doing the right things. Not like your crazy Prime Minister.'

'I know.'

'And the book?'

'Nearly finished now.'

'*Muito bem. Boa noite.*'

*

I have indeed effectively finished the book and have sent it to a friend to read. A few days later we have a long telephone call. I walk around a local car park, usually full of cars, but now, with the pandemic, completely empty and with unexpectedly beautiful wildflowers springing up around its edges. I have it to myself; the streets are all but deserted. I trace its boundary as if I am on a tightrope, looking down at the position of my feet in relation to the ground, and to the abundant weeds, while I listen to my friend's comments from abroad. 'Why call it *The Two Herberts*? It's about Nora.' This suddenly seems obvious. 'The first part about your childhood is nicely done, but it belongs to something else.' I saw the truth of this. 'It's very much about you, I recognise you in it. Are you sure you want it to be so obvious?'

*

I read the whole thing again. All the parts about being isolated during the war, seeing nobody, living quietly, too quietly, are suddenly much more resonant. I have seen no one since returning from London, and spend too much time checking for relative death tolls in different countries. Maria continues to tell me not to go back to Britain, because of its pandemic regime, but when the Foundation understands that this is all going to last longer than originally expected they tell me to go home. I do not have the courage to tell Maria what I am about to do, so I write her a letter. I know it will arrive after I leave.

*

In 1975, Maria got a job as an adjunct professor at Cornell University. She said a formal goodbye to Adam at her farewell drinks, along with all her other colleagues. Delphine made the speech, and Adam gave Maria a small personal gift which, when she unwrapped it at home, she discovered to be a knife. It was a pretty knife, not large, and it came from Japan, but it was a knife. On occasions Maria found herself to be conventional, even superstitious, and this was one of them.

The following Monday was her last working day. She dropped round to Adam's lab in the evening and, as she had hoped, he was the only one left. She walked past the familiar series of tanks and filters and hoisted herself up onto one of the high stools next to his. They both wore their white lab coats and looked most professional even if Maria's patent shoes did not quite reach the footrest. They discussed the nature of the work that she would be doing in New York, and carefully wondered to what extent their fields might cross. 'Let's walk home', said Adam abruptly. They both knew that home meant homes. He was ready to go almost at once, taking off his lab coat and picking up his briefcase while Maria by contrast put on her duffel coat and gloves with some deliberation. They headed up the Byres Road and crossed over into the Botanics and towards the Kibble Palace, which was closed now. Adam led the way down behind it to the Ha'penny Bridge, a spot she hardly knew. The banks were steep and Maria took her steps with care. Adam did not look back. When she had arrived at the bottom they walked together onto the bridge and stood looking down at the River Kelvin, side by side. The water was always a bit scrappy, rarely very forceful. It was a sad kind of river in comparison with the mighty rivers of Portugal. Although the trees grew well and their branches hung over the banks, the spot was irremediably urban. The fetid smell of Himalayan Balsam only exacerbated the sense of insalubrious activity. A more unsuitable place for a farewell she could hardly imagine and, again, she wondered if Adam were impervious to such niceties. 'Impatiens glandulifera', he said. 'Impatiens' he repeated, putting his emphasis on the word as he turned to go.

*

In my letter to Maria I want to convey to her the extent to which she has become important to me, but I know that I can't do so fully before our conversation has advanced a little further. I know she matters to me, but not why. I am moving too fast. I want to ask everything and say everything all at the same time: he loved you, you loved him, you ought to have married him, surely you regret it, surely this is why you cried, surely this is why we cried. But the woman in the slides wants to assure me that my father had been faithful to my mother. This is not what I want to know. I am impatient to be alone with her again. I tell Maria how unexpectedly important it has been to meet her, and how we have both, surely, recognised that there is a bond between us which we had not anticipated. But more than that, I appreciate her humour and careful ministrations, to the extent that she is taking care of me in my isolation rather than the other way around.

I am sorry to disobey her, but it seems sensible to
return to Britain. I don't spell out what that means,
given that I would only be exacerbating the loneliness
of her own situation. It is a long letter, and carefully
done, but it is not a goodbye. I also feel guilty, for no
very clear reason, about leaving. I fly back to England
the next day, arriving at a near-empty airport where I
am escorted across the tarmac by police officers, like
something between a queen and a criminal, and then
head to a single waiting car.

*

Maria was very busy in New York, establishing her
team, applying for grants and working even more
nocturnal hours in the lab than she had in Glasgow.
Many nights she got only a few hours' sleep, and if
she felt uncertain for herself, she felt guilt in relation
to her young colleagues. She literally had no time for
regrets, or even to maintain superfluous correspond-
ences. But a year after going to America, both she
and Adam were invited to Warsaw as the guests of
the Polish Academy. They were collected from the
airport by a driver bearing a card with their names.
As the driver had no English, Adam and Maria
had an almost private discussion about metabolic
cycles. The car pressed forward at what seemed like
a constant speed across flat countryside continu-
ously coated in mud until the driver said 'Here!' and
pulled the car up outside a large nineteenth-century
villa. Tacitly, Adam and Maria had each decided to

confine their discussion to science. There was plenty to talk about. They did not quite agree, but nor did they want to disagree. On return from Poland both went to their labs hoping the results of their tests on the effects of iron would coincide. They both worked hard, but Maria worked harder. In the summer she attended a conference which Adam had organised at the Museum of Zoology in Cambridge. Maria was overwrought with tiredness and her paper went less well than they had both expected. Her results were doubted, and with some reason. Later Adam sent her a birthday card with the confirmatory message she might have wished for, 'Lymphocytes LOVE LOVE LOVE iron.' Maria was not sure which cheered her more: the scientific message, which was such an important one for her work, or the fact that he had remembered her birthday. She told herself not to be silly, but it was true.

*

There is an exceptionally beautiful spring that year. Even in early April it is warm enough to eat outdoors. The trees burst into leaf with a freshness and vigour that we feel has never before been seen. The clear bright light is like a spotlight, illuminating fields and hedges. The motorway is as quiet as a country lane. The country lanes are busier than they have been for a century, with families walking together. No planes fly overhead, or maybe just a large one, every two or three days. They seem to represent a final evacuation.

It is impossible to know if nature is rejoicing, or if, only now, do we have enough time to notice nature at play. Fox cubs chase each other, swans assert their rights; John Clare, it seems, might have felt at home.

\*

Adam went to see Maria just once; or rather, his schedule only once coincided with a visit to see her in her new location. He had already been to the Woods Hole Oceanographic Institute and was on his way back to Britain with barely a day in New York. He took a taxi to the Sloan Kettering and they went out for lunch. They both loved food but had rarely eaten together. Now they had no qualms about making it clear to the other that they were ready to put their known repertoires to audacious effect, eating oysters, *vitello tonnato*, Roquefort, a large green salad and a small chocolate mousse. Adam chose the white wine and Maria the red. One was German and the other, perhaps inevitably, Portuguese. (There was no Portuguese wine on the list, but Maria persuaded the waiter to take a better look in the cellar.) Adam had thought about going to see her lab but in the event, he had to take a taxi directly to JFK. Maria came with him.

The taxi was old, with a sagging leather banquette, and it was hard not to touch each other, especially when the driver took the corner too fast. His two passengers enjoyed this unforced intimacy, and, following the after-effects of lunch, allowed themselves to bask in the brief security of the moment. Adam opened his briefcase and brought out a poorly wrapped LP. It was the recent reissue of Dennis Brain's Mozart Horn Concertos, but Maria was not to know this, because, overcome by the day as a whole, she left the package in the taxi when it finally deposited her back in Manhattan.

\*

Five days after I return I feel brave enough to ring Maria de Sousa. There is no answer. The next day I get a message from a name I do not know: Assunção. It is to say that Maria has been taken into hospital and that their prayers went with her. Every day the news gets a little worse, and the prayers stronger. Nine days later Maria de Sousa dies. In its series about people who have died in the pandemic, the *New York Times* reports that the leading Portuguese scientist who 'focused on the immune system' has 'died after testing positive for the novel coronavirus'. It is ironic. Too, too ironic.

\*

Assunção sends a message to say that Maria has left something for me. We agree that when I return to Lisbon I can collect it. But not immediately. Firstly Assunção has to sort Maria's papers into groups before listing them in any greater detail. Some weeks later she sends a message to say she is ready and we arrange to meet on the terrace of a cafe where I am due to have lunch with a new friend. It is in an area of town unfamiliar to me although I know which bus to take from outside the Assembleia. The bus rattles down the hill and along the Rua Janelas Verdes. Because of the Museu de Arte Antiga I know this first part of the route well, and have often walked its narrow pavements, stepping back against the wall whenever a bus hurtles past. Now my bus continues along past the docks and I get off at Santo Amaro. I arrive early at the Rua Luís de Camões which is just directly up the hill. I know neither the café nor either of the people I am meeting. But I am increasingly used to absorbing strangeness after weeks of pandemic regulations, and it feels somehow right to be in an unknown place.

The terrace is deserted, apart from the now habitual bottles of hand-sanitising gel. I ask the waitress if it would be ok to sit down early, an hour before my lunch-date, and she nods, spraying the table yet again with anti-bacterial cleaner and wiping it down one more time. I sit waiting, peacefully, if mournfully, until I see a woman striding up the hill gesturing towards me with the small and rather scruffy black plastic bag which swings from her hand. I wave back. Assunção joins me on the terrace and we order coffees. I do not want to appear impatient, and in any case prefer to talk at greater length with the woman who seems to have assumed a central role in organising Maria's life. So I do not ask about the gift, or open the bag, which now lies on the table between us, and instead we talk about the larger archive of which Assunção is in charge, which will eventually contain Maria's papers too. After some time I realise there is nothing much more to say and, in any case, Assunçao has to get back to work. Our eyes turn to the bag. Assunção says, confidently, 'You'll know why this is for you. It was meant to go to somebody else, but Maria told me that, after she had met you, it had to go to you. I'll be interested to find out why.'

I wish there were a little more ceremony attached to this final act but there is none to be had, and as soon as I open the plastic bag I see its contents, which are not wrapped. Inside is a very small book, originally leather bound, now with its covers and spine separated from the pages. I finger it carefully. The spine reads: *BEETHOVEN Quartetten 12–17.* Despite its German language front matter, the book was published in London. In the mid-nineteenth century, I guess, as no date is given. It is a disappointing gift. Not because it is small and dilapidated, but because I do not understand it. I had hoped it might hold the key, or at least a hint as to how to answer my question. Assunção looks at my face.

'*Então?*

'*Não faço a minima ideia.*'

Assunção clearly wants more.

'I think Maria believed my father loved music.'

'And he didn't?'

'No, he did like it. But she liked it much more, I am certain of that.'

I am not sure whether to voice my doubts about my father's dissimulation. Instead I ask Assunção to let me know if she finds anything relating to him among Maria's papers. Assunção seems to recognise this as a possibility. She takes her leave.

\*

'Dear Maria', Adam writes to her in his elegant black handwriting.

'Spring is sprung! My crown imperials are resplendent. (They had an especially good feeding last year.) The new Erythronium (Pagoda) is starting its life here. Like you in New York. And, to keep you company, or rather me, I have Portuguese squill! My walks home are now invariably solitary, but my collection of four-leaf clovers is growing.

Here is one I pressed for you'.

\*

I am trying to tie up the loose ends before going back to Britain. One of the final scenarios which I feel needs pursuing is to see the zebrafish in Maria's laboratory at the Champalimaud Centre. I ask Maria's colleague Rita to find a time when I can be given a tour. It would be poignant to return to the enormous and immaculate building and to see her lab only after Maria's death, but somehow the zebrafish still beckon. I arrive and comply with the usual sanitary requirements. In addition to the mask I already have on I don lab coat and plastic slippers. I descend to the basement and am led along brightly-lit right-angled corridors towards the relevant section. Although I have grown up with laboratories full of tiny animals, I have never before seen anything like this: 65,000 zebra fish in serried tanks ranged from floor to ceiling. I can walk between the rows, looking up and down and along at the tanks, my eyes fastening briefly on one tiny fish and then on another as they go about their vital business. Trying to understand why these fish are such good subjects for experiments is both easy and difficult: their transparency clearly makes everything easier to see, but ultimately I understand only that, not unlike us, they are happier when they aren't alone.

*

Before I leave Lisbon that summer I tell Assunção that, if it is acceptable, I would like to take the four-leaf clover in the frame that has been hanging on Maria's wall. As everything is being packed up professionally after my departure I ask if the piece could be delivered to the Foundation. Assunção leaves it in the office at the underground car park, carefully wrapped up, and it is added to the quantity of books and pictures in my office. Weeks later, on a hot August day, the removal men deliver everything I had in Lisbon to my home in England. It takes a long time to sort out 2,000 books, a kitchen's worth of utensils, a wardrobe's worth of clothes and all the other remnants of five years abroad. Almost the last thing to be unwrapped, partly because it hardly seems necessary, is the package containing the four-leaf clover, still in the glossy brown paper which Assunção has used. Once the package is open I discover that Assunção – or somebody else – has taken the leaf out of the frame and put it into a matchbox. Now the frame is empty and its parts are loose. Under the mount is a phrase, and it is one I know: *Tout comprendre, c'est tout pardonner*. I understand nothing, and have nothing to forgive.

\*

I send this new story to the same friend to cast her eye over. My friend says she has enjoyed it, but asks why I have called it Adam. It isn't really about him. It is about Maria, and about me, of course.

**Maria de Sousa** (1939–2020) made her career as a scientist first in Britain and then in the United States before returning to Portugal, where she built on her status as a pioneering researcher by teaching and inspiring others to follow in her steps. She was also a much-respected advocate for the arts and national culture. **Delphine Parrott** (1928–2016) was Professor of Immunology at the University of Glasgow where **Adam Curtis** (1934–2017) was the first Professor of Cell Biology. The careers of all three coincided in Glasgow in the late 1960s.

*The Chelsea Arts Club Balls*, established with the creation of the Club in 1891, were held regularly (in peacetime) at the Royal Albert Hall from 1910–1958.

The excavations at *Baldock* (Herts) began in 1925 and continued for several years, establishing the existence of the Roman town there.

The *Hay's Wharf* project at Tooley St on the Thames was designed by Goodhart-Rendel (1887–1959) and executed 1930–2; Frank Dobson (1886–1963) was commissioned to supply the 39 faience panels. *Donald Hastings* (1900–38) also made reliefs for Goodhart-Rendel, as well as celebrity portraits.

*Unit One* was a group of ten English artists and architects founded in 1933. Their only exhibition (in 1934) was accompanied by a catalogue written by the critic Herbert Read.

*Victor Gollancz* (1893–1967) had links with the art world through the books he commissioned for Ernest Benn, and after founding his publishing company in 1927 he commissioned books broadly aligned in the fight against fascism.

*The Studio. An Illustrated Magazine of Fine and Applied Art* was first published in 1893 and ran through to 1964.

The *New English Art Club* held its first exhibition in 1886 and still exists today.

*Francis Klingender (1907–55)* wrote a variety of books informed by Marxist sociology; among them was *Hogarth and English Caricature* (1944).

*Dora Gordine* (1895–1991) grew up in the Baltic States; she designed Dorich House after marrying Richard Hare, a wealthy Russianist, in 1936.

The caryatid figures for the British Medical Association on the Strand (1908) became the focus of renewed speculation when the building was sold in 1935 and the new owners used their condition as an excuse for their desecration, an event which left *Jacob Epstein* (1880–1959) feeling unsupported, notably by the Royal Academy.

*Eric Gill* (1882–1940) lived at Pigotts, four miles west of Great Missenden, from 1928 until his death.

## Acknowledgements

For their help with this book the author wishes to thank Rita Fior, Margaret Halton, Erica van Horn, Chris Jenkins, Nicola Kalinsky, Cécile and Dominic Lee, Peter St John and Richard Wrigley.

The publisher gratefully acknowledges the Champalimaud Foundation for financial support of this publication.

**PENELOPE CURTIS** grew up in Glasgow. Over the course of a distinguished career in the arts, she has directed the Henry Moore Institute in Leeds, Tate Britain in London, and, most recently, the Gulbenkian Museum in Lisbon. As an art historian, she is especially known for her work on Barbara Hepworth, about whom she has written a best-selling biography, and for many exhibitions on the materials and meanings of sculpture. She was made Chevalier de l'Ordre des arts et des lettres by the French government in 2014, then an Officer of the same order in 2018. Her most recent books are *The Pliable Plane* and *Scale: Sculpture 1945–2000*. *After Nora* is her first novel.

Shumona Sinha
*Down with the Poor!*
trans. Teresa Lavender Fagan

Sylvie Weil
*Selfies*
trans. Ros Schwartz

Clara Schulmann
*Chicanes*
trans. Lauren Elkin *et al.*

Emilienne Malfatto
*May the Tigris Grieve for You*
trans. Lorna Scott Fox

• www.lesfugitives.com •